D1410938

GATEWAYS TO READING TREASURES
CO-BASAL LITERARY READERS

MAGIC AND LAUGHTER

HAROLD G. SHANE
Professor of Elementary Education
and Dean of The School of Education
Indiana University

and

KATHLEEN B. HESTER
Professor of Education
Eastern Michigan University

LAIDLAW BROTHERS • PUBLISHERS
RIVER FOREST, ILLINOIS
SUMMIT, N. J. PALO ALTO, CALIF. DALLAS ATLANTA

GATEWAYS TO READING TREASURES
CO-BASAL LITERARY READERS

A series of seven readers beginning with the Primer *Tales to Read* followed by a book for each grade one through six.

Tales to Read

Stories to Remember

Storyland Favorites

Doorways to Adventure

Magic and Laughter

Words with Wings

Courage and Adventure

Illustrated by

MARY MILLER SALEM
TOM DUNNINGTON
BOB KEYS
VERN McKISSACK
CHARLES MOSER
WILLIAM J. TANIS

ACKNOWLEDGMENTS.—*The authors wish to express their grateful appreciation for permission to adapt and use the following stories:* "The Black Stallion and the Red Mare": Reprinted by permission of the author. "The Boy Who Was Afraid": From *Call It Courage* by Armstrong Sperry. Copyright 1940 by The Macmillan Company. Reprinted by permission of the publishers. "Gold of Norway": Based on reference material and on facts from *Snow Treasures* by Marie McSwigan, E. P. Dutton & Co., Inc. "The Knights of the Silver Shield": From *Why the Chimes Rang and Other Stories,* by Raymond Macdonald Alden, copyright 1906, 1934; used by special permission of the publishers, The Bobbs-Merrill Company, Inc. "In the Beginning": Adapted from *Big Tree* by Mary and Conrad Buff. Copyright 1946 by Mary Marsh Buff and Conrad Buff. Reprinted by permission of The Viking Press, Inc.

PRINTED IN THE UNITED STATES OF AMERICA
2 3 4 5 6 7 8 9 0 9 8 7 6 5 4 3 2

STORIES and POEMS in this BOOK

MAGIC AND LAUGHTER

DESERTS AND WOODLANDS

CHILDHOOD OVERSEAS

THE WORLD'S WONDERS

FROM A SHEPHERD'S HANDS

EXPLORERS BOLD

STORIES YOU'LL LIKE

BEYOND THE SEA

BRAVE DEEDS

LET'S REMEMBER

MAGIC AND LAUGHTER

A daring prince, of the land Rangg Dhune,
Once went up in a big balloon
That caught and stuck on the horns of the moon,
And he hung up there till the next day noon—
When all at once he exclaimed, "Hoot-toot!"
And then came down in his parachute.

James Whitcomb Riley

Ali Baba and the Forty Thieves

A long time ago there were two brothers named Cassim and Ali Baba. They lived in a far-off land. Cassim, the older of the two brothers, had married a rich wife. He had a fine, big home and did not need to work for a living. Ali Baba, the second brother, had married a poor woman. He worked very hard, indeed. Each day he went away from home to cut wood, which he sold in the city.

One day Ali Baba was at work. Suddenly he heard the sound of horses' hoofs. He was frightened and hid behind a tree. There were many bad men in the land and he knew that it was wise to keep out of their way!

Ali Baba just had time to hide before a group of men rode up. They were the forty thieves who had been stealing gold and rich goods from the countryside for many years.

The leader of the thieves stopped his horse at the side of a big hill. "Open, Sesame," he cried, so loudly that Ali Baba could hear him.

No sooner were the words out of his mouth than a magic door opened in the hillside. There was a deep, dark cave behind the door. The forty thieves went into the cave and the door shut behind them.

Ali Baba waited for what seemed a very long time. At last the door opened and the forty thieves came out again.

This time the chief of the band called out, "Shut, Sesame!" The door closed and the men rode away.

Ali Baba wanted to know what was in the cave. After a minute or two he ran up to the side of the hill. Just as he had heard the leader of the thieves do, Ali Baba cried out, "Open, Sesame." Once again the hidden door opened. He went through the doorway. The door closed behind him.

Ali Baba found himself in a huge cave. It was filled with rich goods and gold which the thieves had carried there. Ali Baba trembled with fear. What if the thieves should find him!

Quickly Ali Baba cried, "Open, Sesame," and ran out of the cave. He found the old horse he had left in the woods and led him back to the cave. There he loaded four big bags of gold on the poor beast. Then he hurried from the cave. He called out, "Shut, Sesame," and went home as fast as his horse could travel.

His wife could hardly believe him when Ali Baba told her that they were rich. Her eyes sparkled with joy when she saw the gold.

Now Ali Baba was so happy that he just had to talk about his gold. That was a big mistake. He told his brother, Cassim, where he had found the gold. Ali Baba was so kindhearted that he even told Cassim the words that opened the magic door. And he said that he would give him half of the riches in the cave.

Ali Baba's brother was a mean and selfish fellow. He did not want half of the gold in the cave. He wanted all of it.

Early the next morning, long before the sun was up, Cassim took ten horses. Then he set out for the cave. He planned to load all of the riches on his animals and leave none for Ali Baba.

When he got to the hillside, Cassim cried out, "Open, Sesame!" When the door swung open, he led his horses into the cave. Then the opening in the hill closed behind him.

Cassim hurried to load his horses. He knew it would be dangerous if the forty thieves found him in their hide-out. When he had taken all the gold that his horses could carry, Cassim led the heavily loaded animals to the door.

Suddenly Cassim turned white with fear! He had forgotten the magic words that made the door swing open. He could not get out of the cave!

In a few hours the thieves came back to their hide-out. There they found the trembling Cassim. "Do not kill me!" he cried. "It was not I who found your cave. It was my brother, Ali Baba, who did it. He sent me here to take your gold."

The fierce leader of the thieves laughed. "That is all I wanted to know!" he said. "We will soon visit this brother of yours." Then the chief ordered his men to beat Cassim with heavy sticks. They beat Cassim until they had killed him.

The leader next told his men of a plan to kill Ali Baba because he had found their cave. "In a few weeks Ali Baba will think that he is safe," the chief said. "He may guess that we have caught his brother. But he will not know that his brother told us that Ali Baba found our hiding place."

"We will get a string of horses," the chief went on. "On the horses we will put forty leather oil jars, each one big enough to hold a man. You will get into the oil jars. I will lead the horses to Ali Baba's house. I will tell him that I am a traveling oil-seller, and that there is no room for me to sleep at the inn. Ali Baba will then let me stop for the night at his home.

"Later, when Ali Baba sleeps, I will call you," the chief said. "You will cut your way out of the jars with your knives. Then we will pull Ali Baba from his bed. We will kill him and his wife. Then no one will know about our cave."

Everything happened just as the leader of the thieves had said. When Cassim disappeared, Ali Baba thought that his brother had gone to the cave and been caught. But when he neither saw nor heard of the thieves, Ali Baba decided that he himself was safe.

With the four bags of gold he had taken from the cave he bought a new house and fine clothes. People who had once passed Ali Baba by without a word now treated him like an old friend. He was happy indeed.

Then, late one afternoon, an oil-seller came to Ali Baba's new house. He led a long string of horses. Each one was loaded with large leather oil jars.

Of course, the oil-seller was really the leader of the thieves. Ali Baba had seen him at the cave. But he did not know that his visitor was the same man.

Ali Baba invited the chief to come in when he heard that there was no room for him at the inn. "Please come in," said Ali Baba. "You can have supper with us and a warm bed to sleep in until tomorrow."

"There is plenty of oil in the jars in the yard," the girl said to herself. "I think it will be all right if I take just a little. Then I can cook the supper." And off she went to get some oil in a bowl.

Now it happened that Ali Baba had a wise and beautiful servant girl. She worked as a cook in his house. While she was making supper she found that there was no cooking oil in the kitchen.

When the girl drew near to one of the oil jars, she was greatly surprised to hear someone inside. It was one of the thieves, who said, "Is it time for us to climb out and kill Ali Baba?"

The girl thought quickly. "Not yet," she said, making her words sound deep as if the chief of the thieves were talking. Then she ran to tell her master that there were strange men in the oil jars.

Ali Baba guessed that the thieves were hiding in the jars. "Run and bring the soldiers!" he ordered. "They will be happy to meet our visitors! They will be happy to find the thieves."

In a few minutes the soldiers came on the run, led by the servant girl. Then, very quietly, they crept into Ali Baba's house. There they caught the surprised leader of the thieves. When the leader had been tied up with a rope, Ali Baba led the soldiers to the yard where the oil jars stood along the wall.

"Come out! Come out! It is time!" Ali Baba called. Out popped the thieves—right into the hands of the waiting soldiers.

Ali Baba was so pleased that the little servant girl had found the thieves in the jars that he gave her hand to his son in marriage. There was a great marriage feast. Everyone in the city came. And why should they not, for Ali Baba was now rich and well known for catching the thieves!

And whenever Ali Baba, his son, or even his grandson needed gold there was always the hidden cave to keep them rich to the end of their days.

Strawberry and the Thousand Buffaloes

When people go to the zoo on a warm summer afternoon, many of them stop at a high fence. There is a sign on the fence. People look at the sign.

Then, "Who or what is Strawberry?" the visitors want to know. If they are lucky, and if Mr. Cuddleberry, the zoo keeper, is near at hand, this is the story he tells them.

"Why, friends, Strawberry is that little calf inside the fence," Mr. Cuddleberry begins. "Do you see him there? He has a red mark on his side. See that spot that looks like a strawberry? That's what gave him his name."

"But what is a calf doing in with the buffaloes?" someone is sure to ask.

If he has a little free time, Mr. Cuddleberry just loves to answer that question!

The visitors listen as Mr. Cuddleberry tells his story.

Strawberry was born on a farm a few months ago. When he was old enough to be sold, Strawberry's master decided that he would send him to market. Poor little calf! He didn't know that he was supposed to end up as a meat-roast on someone's table.

In fact, Strawberry was quite pleased when he was loaded on a train. It seemed like a fine adventure to the little fellow when a train took him to the city.

The next day the train brought Strawberry to the yards. There calves and cows and pigs were kept until they were turned into meat-roasts. There were thousands of cattle in the cages. The little calf hoped that he could make friends with some of the other animals.

But, for some reason, Strawberry was put in a cage by himself. Of course, he was more lucky than he knew.

In a short while, Strawberry grew lonely. Then he became very hungry. Someone had forgotten that he had been put in a cage off in a corner. No one came to feed him—but then, no one came to turn him into a meat-roast, either!

Because he was so hungry, Strawberry began to look for a way out of his cage.

In a few minutes, Strawberry found a broken board in the fence. He pushed and pushed. And in a little while he had made a hole that was big enough for him to get through.

Soon the calf found himself on the street. But nowhere did he see anything to eat. Just then a milk wagon rolled past. Strawberry didn't know that it was a milk wagon. But there WAS a picture of a cow on the side. Since he was lonely as well as hungry, Strawberry ran after the wagon.

When the wagon stopped for a minute, the calf managed to climb inside.

To his delight, Strawberry found that the wagon was full of milk! But how did one get it out of the cold, hard glass things that held it?

While Strawberry was trying to decide how to get at the milk, the milkman drove the wagon through the city. Soon he came to a lovely park. As the wagon went into the park, Strawberry knocked over some cases of milk. What a crash they made!

The milkman came running to see what was the matter. "Oh, no!" he cried when he saw the rivers of milk running out of the wagon. "I'll have to pay for this!"

Now Strawberry was a wise calf. He knew that he was in trouble! He jumped out of the wagon and ran off as fast as his legs could carry him. In no time at all he had left the milkman and the wagon far behind.

Strawberry loved the park. The grass was cool and green and, oh, so delicious to eat. Best of all, no one came to trouble him. He just stayed in out-of-the-way corners. No one even saw him.

That night the calf slept among the trees. He didn't open his eyes until the next morning when the sun was up. After he had eaten all the grass he wanted, Strawberry decided to look about the park. The first thing he saw was a high fence.

He had come to the park zoo—only he didn't know it. On the other side of the fence were some of the strangest-looking cows that Strawberry had ever seen.

Also, on the other side of the fence, was a big white piece of salt. And there was nothing in the world that the calf liked better than salt!

Strawberry decided that he just had to have some of the delicious-looking salt. He looked around to find some way to get into the buffaloes' cage.

Then, in a minute or two, Strawberry came to a gate in the fence. The gate was closed. But the lock had not been snapped shut. By chance the calf brushed his nose against the lock and it fell off. The gate swung open. And in no time at all Strawberry was inside.

As soon as the gate was open the buffaloes began to wander outside. They wandered over to the duck pond. They walked past the lion's cage, and ate grass in front of the elephant.

Now it happened that Policeman O'Riley was walking his beat in the park at six o'clock on that fine summer morning. As he went past the duck pond he could not believe his eyes. There along the edge of the water were buffaloes.

Off he ran to the policeman's call-box to telephone for help. "Sergeant Sullivan," he cried, "the park is full of wild buffaloes this morning! They're all over the place—by the duck pond and the lion cages and the elephant house!"

"Now don't be telling me that!" said Sergeant Sullivan. "It's a dream you must be having."

"N-N-No, S-S-Sir," O'Riley cried. "Do be coming down here and see for yourself!"

"Well, I think your head has jumped clean off your big shoulders," said Sergeant Sullivan. "But I'll be right down to see what IS the matter with you!" And Sergeant Sullivan set out for the park as fast as he could go.

By the time that Sergeant Sullivan arrived the buffaloes were wandering past the monkey cages. Some were eating peanuts from the hot dog stand which they had broken into. "It can't be! It just can't be true!" Sergeant Sullivan told O'Riley. Then off he ran to the policeman's call-box to telephone the Police Chief.

"Believe me, Chief," cried Sergeant Sullivan, "there must be hundreds of the beasts all over the place—all of them with horns two feet long."

"Take it easy, you potato-head," the Chief snapped. "I think you're just imagining all this—but I'll be right down!"

By the time the Chief got to the park all the buffaloes had escaped from behind their fence. There seemed to be buffaloes everywhere!

The Police Chief took one look and called out, "O'Riley! Sullivan! Get those animals back in their cage!"

"But how do we get them back?" asked Sergeant Sullivan.

The Chief thought for a minute. Then he said, "Now that's a good question. Maybe I'd better call the Mayor and the Fire Chief. They should know what to do." And off he ran to the policeman's call-box.

"There are a—a thousand buffaloes here in the park!" the Police Chief told the Mayor and the Fire Chief. And when they heard the news both of them came in a hurry riding on the big, red City Fire Engine!

"Oh, dear!" said the Mayor. "This is frightful. Do you think I should send for soldiers—or maybe for cowboys?"

Then the Fire Chief spoke up. "Now just leave this to me and my men," he said.

"I'll GLADLY let you take care of getting the buffaloes back into their cage," said the Mayor. "But what in the world are you going to do?" he asked.

"Just you wait and see!" said the Fire Chief. Then he began to call out orders to the firemen.

The firemen took hoses from the fire engine. When they were ready the Chief called out, "Now turn the water on those beasts." And they did.

The Fire Chief's idea worked beautifully! The water from the hose chased those buffaloes right back inside the fence where they belonged.

All but one buffalo, that is. When the water hit the very biggest buffalo of all he went after the firemen with his horns down.

Now those firemen ran to climb the nearest tree! And when they let go of the hose, the water streamed everywhere. It hit the Mayor and Policeman O'Riley and Sergeant Sullivan. And it poured over the people who had come to see the fun!

Then the big buffalo turned around and quietly walked back inside the fence. His head was high in the air. He looked very proud of himself!

As soon as the last buffalo was inside the fence the Mayor ran up and pushed the gate shut. He was very angry. And well he might be. His fine clothes were ruined. And he looked a sorry sight.

"There!" he said as he snapped the lock shut. "And let me say that as long as I'm the mayor I never want this gate opened again. Not for ANYTHING!"

And it hasn't been opened since.

When Mr. Cuddleberry, the zoo keeper, tells the story of Strawberry and the thousand buffaloes, he always ends his tale this way: "And that's why Strawberry is still inside the fence.

"When the buffaloes came outside, he stayed behind with the salt he loved. And, of course, we could not get him out after the Mayor, himself, said that we must NEVER open the gate."

The Emperor's Nightingale

In days gone by, there was an Emperor in China. As you must know, he was a Chinaman. He lived in a beautiful palace made of colored glass. It stood in the largest and most lovely garden in all the world. Silver bells were tied to the flowers. They made music when the wind blew.

People came from everywhere just to see the Emperor's garden. Some of the visitors even went home and wrote books telling of how great and beautiful it was. They wrote of how the flowers smelled in the soft moonlight when one wandered along the garden paths. They wrote about the silver bells that made music.

Now when men wrote books about the Emperor's garden, all of them would tell of the little Nightingale who sang in the trees. Nothing in the garden, they said, was quite so fine as this small bird's soft song.

One day the old Emperor read a book about his garden. It so happened that he had never heard the Nightingale sing her song. When he read of how beautifully she sang, he called his son, the Prince. "I must hear this bird," he told the boy. "Invite her to come to my palace tonight."

The Prince had much trouble in finding someone who knew the Nightingale. But at last he found a little kitchen girl, one who cleaned the palace pots and pans. She said she knew the bird that sang the soft songs in the garden.

"Please ask the Nightingale to come to see the Emperor," the Prince said to the kitchen girl. "He has never heard her lovely song."

The girl said that she would invite the little bird to come to the palace.

That very night the little Nightingale sang her song for the old Emperor. It was so lovely that the wind stopped blowing the silver bells in the garden in order to listen to its wordless beauty.

Tears of joy came to the eyes of the Emperor as he listened. When the bird had finished, the old man said softly, "What present can I give you for singing to me?"

"I want no present," said the bird. "It is enough to know that you love my music. I will come to the palace each night and sing to you."

After that, for many months, the little Nightingale came to sing for the aged ruler of China. It seemed that he never would grow tired of hearing her song.

Then, one day, the Emperor's brother, who ruled in another kingdom, sent him a present. It was a mechanical bird. All one had to do to make it sing was to wind it up with a key. The old Emperor quickly fell in love with his new mechanical pet. What fun it was to wind it up! How pretty were its golden wings!

Soon the Nightingale from the garden was forgotten. She was almost broken-hearted because the Emperor forgot her. But she did not try to see him again. She just stayed in her favorite tree. And she sang to herself and to the little kitchen girl who always came to hear the Nightingale.

For many a day the Emperor enjoyed his mechanical songbird. Then, quite suddenly, something went wrong! There was a popping sound inside the toy bird and it stopped singing in the middle of its song.

The old man called upon the finest and best watchmakers in all of China. But not one of them could make the mechanical bird sing again.

At last the gold and silver bird was put back in its cage. And there it stood in the Emperor's bedroom. It was pretty to look at, but of no use to anyone.

Then, one day, the old Emperor became ill. He took to his bed and lay very still. There was great weeping in his palace as he grew ever more weak until he could hardly move.

All the Chinese people loved their ruler. One day the wise doctors said that the old Emperor probably never would see the sun rise again. The people heard the news with heavy hearts.

That night, as the old man lay on his bed, he slowly opened his eyes as if for the last time. He looked at the mechanical bird. "Music, music!" he cried. "Please sing once more for me. I have given you gold and rich presents, oh, golden bird, so please sing just once again."

But the silly toy bird sat in its golden cage and did nothing.

The little kitchen girl was weeping in the garden under the Emperor's bedroom window. When she heard the old man, she ran to a far corner in the garden.

The kitchen girl found the little Nightingale sitting in her tree. "Come, oh, come, dear bird!" the girl said. "Let our Emperor hear you sing once more. And do hurry! He is very ill and may never see the sun rise again."

Quickly the dear little live Nightingale flew down to the Emperor's bedroom window. There she began to sing her song of life and hope. Her song was more sweet than ever it had been before.

Color came back to the old Emperor's tired, white face. "Go on, dear Nightingale, go on," he said softly when she stopped for a moment. And the little bird sang on. Again the song was so lovely that the very wind stopped blowing in order to listen.

When the Nightingale had finished her song, the old man said, "You must always stay with me. You may sing what you please. And I will break the mechanical bird into a thousand pieces."

"Oh, no," said the Nightingale. "The toy golden bird did its best as long as it could. Keep it as you have done till now. But I will come each night and sing by your window. I will sing to you of love and joy and the good things in life."

With these words the Nightingale sang one last song, then flew away into the night. When she had gone the Emperor fell into a sound and restful sleep.

The next morning the servants came to see if the old man had lived to see the sun rise. They opened the door, oh, so quietly. There they found the Emperor standing, yes, STANDING by the window!

The Emperor turned from the window as the sun rose. There was new color in his face and his eyes were sparkling. With a beautiful smile the Emperor said:

"Good Morning!"

The King's Fool

Long, long ago—so long that none can tell—in every palace there was a king's fool. His work was to amuse the king and all the people who lived in the palace. Sometimes he told jokes to make the king laugh. Sometimes he played tricks on the people. And often he told stories which only wise men could answer.

If you are as wise as the king's men, you will know the answers to these stories. If some are too hard for you, peek back on page 237 to find the answers.

●

How many sides are there to a tree?

● ●

Why was the elephant the last animal to leave Noah's Ark?

● ● ●

What King Arthur had before, poor thing!
What Proserpina had behind, poor thing!
What the Emperor never had at all, poor thing!
What was it?

● ● ● ●

A farmer was driving home his cows. There were two cows in front of a cow, two cows in back of a cow, and a cow in the middle. What was the smallest number of cows the farmer could have had?

● ● ● ● ●

A man saw something very strange. Two horses were standing in a field. One was looking north and the other one was looking south. How do you think each could see the other without turning around?

DESERTS AND WOODLANDS

In the Beginning

We, the Giant Trees, are old;
Older than any living thing
On earth.
Long, long before the Cave Man
Made his stone arrows
In the darkness of his cave,
Long, long before then,
Our fathers lived.
They lived all over the world.

I came from them.
A seed,
A seedling,
A GIANT.
From a forgotten time,
From the morning of the World.

Why Winter Comes

The Story of Proserpina

In days long gone by, people did not know much about the world. They made up stories to explain why the rain fell and why the sun traveled across the sky. Here is a tale the Romans told some two thousand years ago. It is their story of why the world turns cold and bare in the wintertime.

. . . . .

There was once a Roman goddess named Ceres. She was the goddess of all growing things. Because of her the flowers blossomed, the leaves turned green on the trees, and the corn grew tall and ripe in the fields.

Ceres had a beautiful daughter named Proserpina. She loved the girl more than anything else on the earth or in the sky. One day Ceres was away, looking after her trees and flowers. Proserpina was playing with some friends.

The girls were in the middle of a green field making flower chains when they heard the pounding of horses' hoofs. A dark man came by, driving a team of wild and coal-black horses. He was good-looking as only a god could be. He was Pluto, king of the underworld.

When he saw the beautiful Proserpina, Pluto fell in love with her. He took her by the arm and drove off with her while her friends cried out in fear.

Although Proserpina was weeping, Pluto did not seem to see her tears.

"Please, please take me back," the girl cried.

"Never!" snapped Pluto. "I have as much right as the other gods to have a beautiful wife. I knew that you would not be queen of my dark underworld of your own free will. That is why I had to steal you away!"

Pluto drove fast to the faraway mountains. He waved his hand and the mouth of a cave opened by magic in the mountain wall. The team of black horses darted inside.

Proserpina cried out in fear as the cave mouth closed behind them. Down, down, down, Pluto carried her to his dark underground kingdom.

When Ceres returned home to find her lovely daughter gone, she hardly knew what to do. Even with all her magic to help her she could not learn what had happened to her child.

Ceres began to wander over the earth looking for Proserpina. Soon no one would have guessed that she was a goddess. Her once beautiful clothes grew old and dirty. Those who saw her thought she had lost her mind, for she kept asking everyone, "Where is my child? Have you seen Proserpina?"

At last, after many months, Ceres came to a small stream. The cool, sparkling water came from a small opening in the rocky mountainside. There, on the bank of the stream, was the narrow crown of gold that Proserpina had worn the day she disappeared.

Ceres took the little crown in her hands. She was so sad that her tears fell into the stream. Then, quite suddenly, the goddess thought she heard words coming from the water of the stream!

Yes, the stream was telling her something! She listened, oh, so carefully.

"Oh, Ceres," came the words. "I make a long journey under the ground before my waters burst from these rocks. As I passed through the underworld, a beautiful but sad young queen gave me the little crown of gold. She asked me to carry it to the sunlit world where you might find it."

Ceres knew at once that it was Pluto who had carried off her daughter to be his queen. She knew, too, that only Jupiter, king of the gods, could help her. Quickly the goddess made her way to Jupiter's palace.

When Ceres saw Jupiter she cried, "Listen, O father of gods and men. What do you hear on earth?"

Jupiter listened. Then he said, "Why, I hear men weeping and cattle crying out in hunger. What is wrong? Who has hurt my people on earth?"

"It is I who this day have hurt them. I, who was once man's best friend, have done this thing. I have killed the trees and flowers. I have turned the green corn to brown. Nothing on earth will grow until you promise to bring my daughter back from the underworld to which dark Pluto has taken her!"

At first Jupiter knew not what to say or do. He did not wish to anger his brother, Pluto. Yet neither did he wish to let the earth stay brown and bare.

At last the king of the gods spoke. "I will promise this, O Ceres. I will go myself to the dark underworld and bring Proserpina back to the world of green and living things she loves. But I can do so only if she has eaten no food while she has been in the dark kingdom of Pluto, my brother." With these words Jupiter took himself off to the underworld.

When Jupiter reached the underworld, he called Pluto and Proserpina to him. He told them of his promise to Ceres. Then he said, "Tell me, Proserpina, have you eaten one bit of food since your husband, Pluto, carried you here?"

The young queen's face grew even more white than it had been before. Of all the food that had been placed before her she had wanted only to have one piece of fruit. And of that she had eaten but six seeds. With her eyes on the floor she said that she had eaten these six seeds.

For two long minutes Jupiter said no word. At last he spoke. "Now hear this," he said. "For each of those seeds you must spend one month underground every year. The other six months you may live in the world of sunlight and flowers."

Every year thereafter Proserpina spent six months as queen of Pluto's dark kingdom. Ceres, her mother, would shut herself up and would not let the grass grow or the flowers blossom. For six months the earth lay cold and bare.

Then, each year, with the return of Proserpina, the fields would turn green. The earth was no longer cold and dark and bare. Everywhere buds would burst on the trees, and flowers would flame to life with their many colors.

On the farms and in the towns, the people would cry out in joy, "She comes! She comes! Proserpina comes. Spring is here!"

The Black Stallion and the Red Mare

At first Donald lay very still in the tall grass. He dug his toes into the dry earth and watched the band of wild horses eating grass in his father's fields far below. From where Donald lay, he could see that there were many horses in the band.

Donald had heard about the horses. But he had never before had the good luck to see them. They were known over hundreds of miles of the West. They had led many a horse away from the farms over which they traveled. Once in that band, the horse was lost to his master.

In all the grasslands for a hundred miles about, every boy had a dream. It was a dream of riding the great black stallion, the leader of the band of wild horses. Donald could see the great horse now. He was beautiful. The animal was a huge creature with long, strong legs and a black coat that shone in the sun.

Down-wind from the horses a red mare stood. The stallion saw the mare and called to her. She waited until he was at her side. Then she followed him back to the band.

Donald knew that his father and other farmers for miles around wanted to round up the wild horses. At the same time, the boy loved all wild, free creatures. He wished in his heart that they might never be caught.

But Donald knew he must tell his father that the horses were close at hand. Somewhat sadly he crept down the hill from his hiding place and ran home.

"Good boy!" said Donald's father quietly when he learned that the wild horses were in the hills nearby. "We will ride to other farms tonight and pass the word to our friends and neighbors. Then we'll start after the horses at sunrise."

The next day, men on horseback came from miles around to take part in the hunt. The dust was thick as the pounding hoofs of their horses dug the dry earth when the chase began. The black stallion led or drove his wild band well. The first day only a few of the smallest horses were taken.

At sunup on the second day the wild horses were seen moving to the west. They, too, had rested during the night. One hundred feet ahead of them ran the great stallion, his long, black tail snapping in the wind. Close to his side ran the lovely red mare.

After the first day's chase, and a night under the stars, Donald had ridden home. Not that he wanted to go back! But there was work to do at home while his father was away leading the hunt. And Donald had to return to school.

The great roundup continued. Each day more and more horses were caught. Soon the men saw that the black stallion was leading his band in a great circle. Over and over again he covered the same ground. The wild horses stopped at the same water holes and ate in the same rich grasslands.

Once the men saw that the horses were traveling the same path over and over again, they worked out a plan. Men with fresh horses were stationed along the way. Soon the wild band had time neither to eat nor to rest. When the poor beasts outran one group of horsemen, a fresh team of riders would continue the chase around the great circle.

As the great chase continued into the second week, everyone grew more and more interested. In every little town, the people talked of nothing else. At school the children played roundup whenever they had any free time.

The wild horses grew more tired and weak with each passing day. Each day more and more were caught. Near the end of the second week, Donald's father rode into the farmyard. As he slowly got off his horse, the boy ran up to him. "Dad, they haven't got the black stallion and the red mare, have they?" he asked. Donald could hardly wait to hear his father's slow answer.

"No, Son," he said, "but those two are the only horses still free. We'll get them tomorrow. You may come along and see the end of the chase."

That night, at supper, Donald's father said, "That was a great band, Son. Never again will we see the like of them. The two that are left are great horses. Their legs are like steel. And the black stallion is a wise fellow. He has had a hundred chances to get away. Yet he would not leave his band without a leader."

After a moment he spoke again. "Even now the stallion could get away if he would leave the red mare. But he will not. It is strange how they keep together. He always waits until she is at his side," he said thoughtfully.

The next morning, in the cold early light, the men crept up on the black stallion and the red mare. They were drinking at the water hole where they had been sleeping during the night. The great black animal saw that they were in danger. He and the mare darted off with the riders at their heels.

Both of the fine horses were very tired. Their coats were covered with dust and dirt, and their eyes were red from too little sleep. Only the wish to be free and their great hearts kept them going.

At last the red mare could run no longer. One of the riders caught her legs in his rope and she crashed to earth in the dust. Even then the great black stallion might have escaped. Instead he stood by the mare, his eyes flaming more with anger than with fear.

Then, suddenly, the long chase was over. A rope brought the stallion down, and he struggled wildly and fruitlessly as the riders closed in on him. Never again would he wander the West as king of his wild band.

Donald saw it all, and tears blinded his eyes as the brave horse gave up his struggle and lay still. The sun was far down in the sky as the great hunt ended.

Donald's father had been looking closely at the two horses. Suddenly he called, "Son, come here." When Donald drew near, he said softly, "Do you know that this mare is blind? That is why the black stallion would not escape while he could. He would not leave her alone in a world of darkness and fear."

A week later Donald and his father stood by the fence watching the black stallion and red mare. They were not the same wild, free creatures, but they were still fine horses.

Donald's father turned to him. "I thought they had won the right to stay together," he said to the boy. "I've brought them home for you. They are yours, Donald, and I know you will be good to them."

Life in the West

Ho! brothers come here and listen to my story,
Merry and short will the tale be:
Here, like an emperor, I rule in my glory,
Master, am I, boys, of all that I see.
Where once stood a forest, a garden is smiling;
The grasslands and wastelands are fields no more,
And there rises the smoke of my castle, calling
The children, who gather like knights at the door.
Then enter boys, cheerily, boys, enter and rest,
The land of the heart is the land of the West.
Oho, boys!—oho, boys!—oho!

CHILDHOOD OVERSEAS

If I could climb a higher tree
Farther and farther I should see,
To where the grown-up river slips
Into the sea among the ships.

Robert Louis Stevenson

Great Thoughts of Wise Men of Other Lands

"Take care of the minutes,
for the hours will take care of themselves."

Lord Chesterfield

"Yesterday will not be called again."

J. Skelton

"Let me get through today and I shall not fear tomorrow."

St. Philip Neri

"Nothing is impossible to a willing heart."

John Heywood

"*Wishers* and *woulders* be no good householders."

John Heywood

Gold of Norway

This is a story about some brave boys and girls in Norway. It is a tale of how they saved $9,000,000 in gold when the Germans came into their country during World War II. We know that the gold was saved because a ship from Norway brought the $9,000,000 to our side of the ocean in 1940. However, we are not sure just what the children did to trick the Germans. This is the story of how they *might* have done it.

Eric and Kirsten Neteland lived in a small fishing town in Norway. The town was near the ocean. Great mountains rose around the little houses. During the long winters the cold wind sang down the chimneys.

Eric and Kirsten's father worked in the bank in their town. One night Mr. Neteland came home with a sad face. He said very little and sat for a long time in front of the warm fire. Even during dinner he was not as pleasant as he was most of the time. He seemed to be thinking of something that troubled him.

After the table had been cleared, Mr. Neteland said, "Eric and Kirsten, please get your coats. I want you to come with me for a walk in the snow."

They walked for a long time. They walked out of the town and through the snow-covered woods. At last they came to a clearing, an open place among the trees. Mr. Neteland looked around carefully. Then he sat down on a snowy log.

"I want you to listen to this," he said. "Listen carefully, because I need your help." This is what he said as the children sat at his feet.

"You know that the Germans have come into our country because we are at war. Norway is a small land and there is very little we could do to stop them.

"Before the Germans came to Norway, our king sent some of our country's gold to my little bank. Only a few men know that there is $9,000,000 hidden under the snow in the woods. It is near the hill down which you slide on your sleds," Mr. Neteland told the children.

"The German soldiers must not get their hands on this gold," their father went on. "We must send it over the ocean where it will be safe until after the war is over. A few of us have been thinking of ways to carry the gold past the German soldiers' camp near the ocean. We believe that only you and some of the older children from the town school can trick the Germans. You can hide the gold near the ocean where one of our ships can get it some dark night."

Eric and Kirsten were glad to help save the gold. But they knew it would be dangerous if the German soldiers caught them doing it. In the weeks that followed a plan was worked out.

Each day the older children from the town school would go sledding on the big hill. Then, one or two at a time, they would steal off into the deep woods where the gold was hidden. With the help of Mr. Neteland or other men from the town, they would wrap a few large pieces of gold in an old cloth or in a coat. Then they would tie it on their sleds and go back to play.

When everyone had a load of gold, the children would go down the mountain. They would pull their sleds past the German soldiers' camp and walk several miles along the ocean. There they would dig a hole in the snow and cover the gold.

Last of all, the children would make a snow man to mark the place where the gold was hidden. When their work was done, the children would again walk by the German camp and go to their homes.

Late at night several men from the village would steal quietly through the woods and mountains. They would dig up the gold once again and take it to a hidden cave. The cave faced the ocean, and in it was a small boat. The men put the gold in the hold of the boat. When all the gold had been moved there, the men planned to go out on the ocean to meet a large ship. This ship would carry the gold across the ocean where the Germans could not get it.

All went well for several weeks. Every day or two Eric, Kirsten, and a few of their friends would pull their loaded sleds past the German camp. None of the soldiers even dreamed that the gold of Norway was sliding past their very noses! Indeed, the Germans became used to seeing the children come by. They would wave their hands and call "Hello."

At last there was only one more load of gold to carry. And a good thing it was! Spring was coming and the snow soon would be gone.

Only eight of the large pieces of gold needed to be packaged and taken past the camp. Eric and Kirsten decided to take the last load themselves. All went well until they came to the Germans' camp. There Eric and Kirsten met a huge German sergeant on the road. He looked big and dangerous in his long winter coat.

As bad luck would have it, Kirsten's sled turned part way over. Kirsten's coat, which covered the gold, slid a little to one side. For a second or two, the sunlight sparkled on a corner of one of the pieces of gold.

Quickly Kirsten righted the sled and pulled her coat over the corner of the gold. Then she and Eric walked on, pulling the sleds as if nothing had happened.

The German sergeant was not a quick thinker. If he had been, he would have stopped the children at once. As it was, he scratched his foolish head for several minutes.

"It couldn't be," the big sergeant said to himself. "It just couldn't be that those children are carrying some of the gold that we have never found. Or could it be?"

At last he decided to call four soldiers who stood near by. "Follow me," he ordered, and hurried after the children.

Meanwhile Eric and Kirsten struggled through the snow with their heavy load.

"Listen to me, Kirsten," Eric said, breathing hard. "If the Germans follow us, I will try to lead them away. Then you must run and tell Father what has happened. He will know what to do."

When they came to the clearing in the woods, Kirsten and Eric hid the gold under the snow. They were just finishing a small snow man to mark the hiding place when the German sergeant and his soldiers caught up with them.

Both Eric and Kirsten were very frightened as the sergeant walked over near the snow man and angrily said to them, "What did you have on your sleds?"

Neither child spoke a word.

"Answer me!" the German barked. But Eric and Kirsten did not speak.

The sergeant was not quite sure what he should do. Then, to Eric's fright, the big soldier began to kick the snow man to bits. The snow there just barely covered the gold. Suppose the sergeant should uncover it!

Quickly, the boy ran a few steps and made a snowball. "German pig!" he cried, and threw the snowball at the sergeant.

The big sergeant was very angry as he cleaned the snow from his face and coat. "Go after that boy," he snapped at the soldiers. Then all five of the men began to chase Eric who ran for the woods like a deer. They quite forgot Kirsten who turned and ran in the other direction.

Eric led the soldiers a merry chase through the deep snow. He was so light that the hard snow held him up while the soldiers sank in over their knees. In no time he had left them far behind. By the time the moon rose he had made a big circle and returned to his home.

Kirsten was inside when Eric got to the house. She had told Mr. Neteland all that had happened. So all the family was happy to see Eric again, as you can imagine.

While Eric drank a cup of hot chocolate, his father explained what happened after Kirsten brought home the news. He told him that men from the town had gone to get the last of the $9,000,000 hidden under the fallen snow man which the sergeant had kicked over.

"This very night," he then continued, "our little fishing boat will carry the gold of Norway to one of our ships that is waiting for it on the ocean. Now we have only one thing to fear."

"What is that?" Kirsten and Eric said in one breath.

"We must hope that the sergeant and his men do not follow your footsteps in the snow when there is light to see by in the morning. If they do, the tracks will bring them to our door."

But that night there was a heavy fall of snow. It covered Eric and Kirsten's tracks and the Germans never did learn where they had gone.

Not till after the war was over did the Germans learn that the children of a little fishing village had tricked them and saved the gold of Norway. And by that time it did not matter, for the Germans had been chased out of Norway.

Out With the Goats

Heidi is a girl who lived some years ago in Switzerland. Her mother and father had been killed when Heidi was very little. At first her uncle took care of her. Then, after a while, he left her with her grandfather who lived high up on the side of a mountain. This story tells of what Heidi did the first day after she came to live on the mountainside.

Heidi woke up the next morning to hear someone calling. It was Peter, the boy who took care of her grandfather's goats. "Get up, sleepyhead!" he called. "Do you want to go up the mountains with the goats?"

"Indeed I do!" cried Heidi. "Thank you, Peter, for calling me."

Then, while the girl was washing and dressing, her grandfather asked Peter to bring his bag and come into the house. Peter, in surprise, did as he was told. He put the bag, which held his small dinner, on the table. Inside it the old man put a large piece of cheese and an even larger piece of bread. It was more bread and cheese than the boy had to eat.

"That is for Heidi," said the grandfather. "And give her two bowls of milk from my goats. When you go up the mountain, be sure that she does not fall over any of the rocks!"

The children joyfully set out to climb the mountain. They drove the band of goats before them.

The mountains in Heidi's part of Switzerland were as beautiful as anything in the world that day. Their sides were bright with summer flowers. As she picked the flowers the girl quite forgot both Peter and the goats.

Poor Peter soon found that he had to watch both Heidi and his goats. At last he called out angrily, "Where are you, Heidi?"

"Over here!" came her words from somewhere far off.

The boy found her at last. "Come along here and stay with me," he ordered. "I don't want you falling over the rocks as you gather those silly flowers."

At last the children and the goats reached a green field high up on the mountainside. While the goats were eating and playing about, Peter opened the bag of food he had carried.

When he had milked a goat, he called Heidi. "Stop jumping about," he said. "It is time to eat."

"Is the bowl of milk for me?" she asked.

"Yes, and so are the biggest pieces of bread and cheese," Peter told her.

When Heidi had finished her milk, she broke off big pieces of her bread and cheese and gave them to Peter. When he was sure that she really meant him to have them, Peter gladly took every bit. He had not had so much to eat in as long as he could remember.

After he had eaten, Heidi asked, "Do the goats have names?"

"Yes," said Peter. "I call this one Little Whiteface. That one, with the mark on his head, is Black Star, and the brown fellow is Mr. Chocolate. The two little ones I call Candy and Peanuts, and the big black fellow is Pluto."

While they were talking, some of the goats had begun to wander away. Suddenly Peter jumped to his feet. Without a word he ran through the band of goats and toward the edge of the meadow. There the mountain dropped down for a thousand feet. Heidi ran after Peter. "What is wrong?" she cried.

Peter stopped at the very edge of the drop-off. "Look," he cried. "Before I could get here, Little Whiteface climbed down on that narrow bit of rock! Now she is afraid to climb back! How can I ever save her? If she falls into the valley and is killed, your grandfather will beat me."

After a minute, Peter said bravely, "Well, I must try and climb down there. If only I had brought a rope!"

"Wait, Peter!" said Heidi. "Hold on to my hand. Let me go part way down with some flowers. Little Whiteface loves these blossoms. Perhaps I can make her come back up if I hold them in front of her nose!"

Since he had no better idea, Peter agreed to try Heidi's plan.

Oh, so carefully, Heidi climbed down near Little Whiteface while Peter tightly held her hand. Would the little goat come to get the flowers? Yes! The plan worked. Slowly Heidi led the goat out of danger. A minute later and they were both safely back on the grass at the top of the steep mountainside.

When he had caught his breath, Peter picked up a stick. He raised his hand to strike the little goat.

Heidi cried out, "Please don't hurt Little Whiteface. She didn't know the trouble she was making."

On the way home Peter said, "You will make a fine mountain girl, Heidi. You love the mountains, don't you! And you know how to take care of yourself and what to do when there is trouble. I wouldn't have thought of using flowers to get Little Whiteface back where it was safe."

Heidi was very happy when she went to bed that night. Why, Peter had even asked her to climb up with the goats again the next day! All night she slept on her bed of sweet hay, dreaming of mountains that show brightly against the sky.

Dick Whittington and His Cat

Long ago in England there lived a poor boy whose name was Dick Whittington. He had no mother or father. And he had to live on the food that people gave him.

When he was ten or eleven years old, Dick decided to go to London. He had heard many tales about this wonderful city and was certain that he could make a fine living once he got there.

The coach to London traveled through Dick's town. The boy got a ride to the great city by helping the coachman feed and care for the horses on the trip.

When he got to London, the coachman gave Dick a little money and sent the boy on his way. The money was soon gone. Then Dick felt the fierce hunger that boys have.

For two days the boy wandered without food in the dark and dirty streets of the great city. Then, on the night of the third day, he came to the house of a rich merchant. He asked for work or food, but the cook told him to go away.

Poor Dick was so weak from hunger that he slid to the steps and lay there. Just then the merchant rode up in his coach. "What are you doing here, you lazy fellow?" he cried.

"Give me a little food. Please, a little food," Dick said weakly.

The merchant looked more closely at Dick. "God forgive me," he said. "The boy is hungry." Then the kindhearted man carried Dick into his home. He gave him food and a place to sleep. When Dick was able to work, he was given a job cleaning pots and pans in the kitchen.

Dick's bedroom was a mean little place under the roof. It was full of rats and mice. With the first money he earned, the boy bought a cat. Dick kept the animal in his room. She was a fine mouser. In no time at all, she had killed every rat and mouse in the place.

Whenever the merchant sent one of his ships on a long journey, he called his servants together in the great hall in his home. He would then ask them if they wished to send something on his ship to be sold in lands far over the ocean. When the goods were sold, they usually brought a fine price. And, in this way, the servants could make quite a lot of money.

Everyone sent something to be sold except Dick. "Have you nothing to send, my boy?" the kindly merchant asked.

"I have nothing in the world," said Dick, "except my cat."

Dick was very sad at the thought of losing his cat. But he decided to send her to be sold when the merchant invited him to do so.

Once the cat was gone, however, life was not the same for Dick. He felt sad and alone. The cook was cross and mean to him when he worked in the kitchen. At last Dick made up his mind to leave London and go back to his little home town in the west of England.

Very early one morning, Dick got out of bed. He tied his few clothes into a small package and crept out of the house. He was on the road by the time the sun came up.

When Dick reached the edge of London Town, he heard the great bells of the city ringing. They seemed to be telling him something. And he stopped to listen.

He seemed to hear the bells say:

"Turn back, turn back,
Dick Whittington.
Three times, three times
you'll be
The *Mayor* of London
Town!"

Dick listened to the promise of the bells. For several minutes he listened to their silvery words. Then he turned back to London.

He started to walk. But soon he was running. He was back at the merchant's house before anyone else was out of bed. No one even knew that he had been gone. He ran to his room.

All the time that Dick was thinking about leaving London, his cat had been traveling across the ocean. The winds carried the ship to a far land where there was a rich kingdom. The captain of the ship sent word to the king saying that he had fine goods to trade and sell.

The captain was invited to the king's palace to show his trade-goods. After he had bought many things, the king gave a great feast for the captain and his men. It was a wonderful dinner, indeed! The food was carried in on plates of gold and in bowls of silver.

But before the captain and his men could eat, great bands of rats and mice ran into the huge room. They even ran off with food from the plates on the table!

The surprised captain turned to the king and asked, "Do these creatures always give you so much trouble?"

"Indeed they do," the king replied. "I would give half of my kingdom to be rid of them."

The captain thought of Dick Whittington's cat. "Why," he said, "I have a wonderful beast from England on my ship. She will rid your palace of rats and mice in a hurry!"

The rich king was overjoyed. "Bring me this creature and I will load your ship with gold," he said.

The captain made believe that he could not bear to part with the cat. "But I cannot sell her," he cried. "She keeps my ship clear of rats."

But the king would not take no for an answer. He promised even more gold for the cat. The captain at last agreed to sell her. His eyes sparkled at the thought of all the gold the cat would bring.

While one of the men from the ship ran to get the cat, the table was spread for another feast. Again the rats and mice darted in as before. As soon as the cat was set free, however, she went to work. In no more than a minute she had cleared the great hall of every rat and mouse.

Then, with a loud mew, the cat walked over to the king and brushed against him in a most friendly way.

The king was so delighted with the cat that he gave more gold for her than the captain's whole shipload of goods was worth. Then, with a fair wind to blow his ship, the captain returned to England.

The rich merchant was full of joy when the ship reached London. Never before had he made so much money! He took the gold that the king had paid for Dick Whittington's cat and hurried home.

As soon as he reached home the merchant called his servants to the great hall. He gave each one a fair part of the money for which his trade-goods had been sold.

At last he called, "Dick Whittington." When the boy stood before him he said, "This box of gold was paid for your cat. It is all yours, my boy, and you are now a rich man."

At first Dick could not believe his ears. Then he fell on his knees and thanked his master for his kindness. Never again would he be cold because he had too few clothes to wear in winter.

In the years that followed, the rich merchant raised Dick as if he were his own son. Later, as a man, Dick entered the merchant's business. And at last he even married the old man's lovely daughter.

And what of the promises the bells had made to Dick Whittington:

"Three times, three times
you'll be
The Mayor of London
Town!"

Why they came true! The poor country boy who became Sir Dick Whittington was three times chosen as Mayor of the greatest city in all England.

THE WORLD'S WONDERS

One time Winnie ask her Ma,
At the winder, sewin',
What's the wind a-doin' when
It's a-not a-blowin'?

James Whitcomb Riley

Our Wonderful World

Great, wide, wonderful, beautiful world,
With the beautiful water about you curled,
And the wonderful grass upon your breast—
World, you are beautifully dressed!

Oh, you are so great, and I am so small,
I tremble to think of you, World, at all;
And yet, when I said my prayers today,
A wee voice within me seemed to say:
"You are more than the earth, though you're
not a lot;
You can love and think, and the world cannot."

A Volcano Is Born

One day early in 1943 a Mexican Indian farmer was working in his small fields. He moved about in the sun planting corn seeds in every square foot of earth. His wife worked near his side.

It was warm and the woman stopped her work to rest. Suddenly she called to her husband. "Pedro," she said, "are my eyes playing tricks on me? Or is the middle of our field falling into the earth?"

Pedro ran to her side. He looked at the field with care. "Yes," he said at last. "There is a hollow place in the field. It was not there a little while ago."

"Now look!" cried the woman. "There is white smoke or steam coming from the hollow."

As Pedro looked on in surprise, he and his wife felt the earth move under their feet. At the same time they heard a loud noise. It sounded like a giant waterfall below them.

"I am afraid!" the woman cried. Even as she spoke the earth trembled again. The next minute black smoke burst from the hollow spot in their field. Flames shot high into the sky.

The Indians dropped their tools and ran toward Paricutin, the sleepy little Mexican town which was nearby.

On the road to Paricutin, Pedro and his wife ran into some of their friends and neighbors. "What was that great noise?" they asked. "Where is all the smoke coming from?"

"It is frightful," cried Pedro's wife and burst into tears. "Our beautiful farm is blowing up in smoke."

"Run! Run for your lives, or we will all be killed," Pedro called out.

The earth began to tremble everywhere. And the people ran for the hills as if a tiger were at their heels.

That night, from the hilltops, the Indians looked down on their fields below. Bright flames lighted the dark sky. And the earth under their feet rolled so much that it was difficult for them to stand.

The simple Mexican Indians of Paricutin did not know it, but they were seeing something that man had never seen before. A volcano was being born in front of their very eyes. When the sun came up in the morning, they saw a great black blanket of smoke below them.

Early in the day a man arrived from Mexico City, the largest city in Mexico. He had been sent to study the new volcano. His name was Doctor Bell. Two soldiers were with him.

As the day passed, Doctor Bell kept watch over the volcano. He also told the Indians that volcanoes were caused by fires inside the earth which sometimes burst through to the surface.

Late in the afternoon the earth began to tremble even harder than before. Huge rocks were thrown up to the sky. They were red hot!

Then an even stranger thing began to happen. A black hill began to grow in the middle of what had once been poor Pedro's cornfield. As Doctor Bell and the Indians looked on, the hill grew and grew. Soon it was fifty feet high—as tall as a five-story building. It was so hot that it looked like a hill of fire.

As the sun dropped low in the sky the hill became higher and higher. Soon it looked like a small mountain and towered over one hundred feet in the smoke-filled air. Flames and smoke still poured forth from the volcano's mouth. Out poured melted rock called *lava* which ran down its sides.

As the days grew into weeks the baby volcano grew ever larger. Soon it was a baby no longer. The lava streamed into the little town of Paricutin and covered it. Pedro and all of the other farmers sadly moved away. They could work in their old fields no more. When the volcano quieted down and was less dangerous, Doctor Bell and the soldiers left also.

The Mexican people called the big new-born volcano Paricutin after the town that once stood in the cornfields. Travelers came from near and far to see the fire and smoke and to watch the slow-moving lava.

It was frightening to see hot rocks blown high in the air and to feel the earth tremble under one's feet. Yet in its wild way Paricutin was beautiful, as it steamed in the sun or burned red against the night sky. In 1952, the last hot rocks were thrown out and there was no more lava.

As one looks upon the world's newest volcano, he cannot help but feel that man is small and weak. And how great our wide world is, with fires burning at its heart!

A Trick of the Eyes

"Seeing is believing!"

"Very well," said Peter, "then I can show you that you have a hole in your hand through which you can see things."

Here is how Peter showed Donald that he could look straight through his hand.

Roll a piece of writing paper into an inch roll. This is the way it will look.

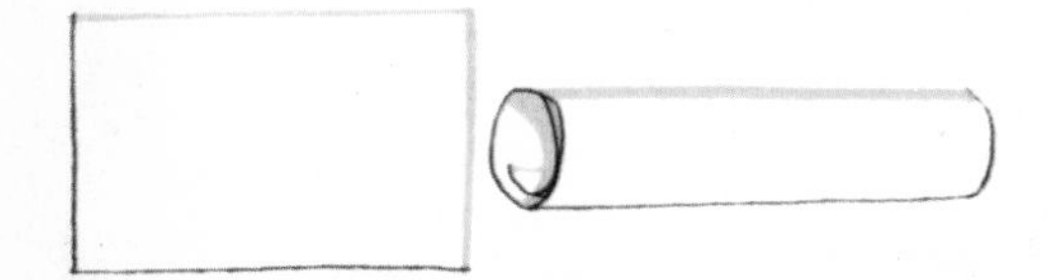

Now look through the paper roll with your right eye.

Hold your left hand beside the roll and close to the lower end of it.

Keep both eyes open. Look through the roll with your right eye and look at your hand with your left eye.

Do you see the hole in the middle of your hand? And can you see something on the other side through the hole?

Do you believe it?

Archimedes and the Golden Crown

More than two thousand years ago the king of a city in Greece wanted a new crown. He took a large piece of gold from his strong room and gave it to a man who made beautiful things of silver and gold.

"Make me the most lovely crown in the world," the king ordered. "I will wear it at my great feasts."

The king was not sure that the crownmaker would use all of his fine gold. He weighed the gold before he gave it to the crownmaker. Later he planned to weigh the crown so as to be sure that all the gold had been put into it.

After several weeks the workman brought the new crown to the king. It was, indeed, beautiful. The king placed it on his head where it sparkled even in the poorly lighted hall of the palace.

The king sent the workman on his way with a small bag of gold pieces. Then the ruler hurried to his strong room to weigh the crown. He found that the crown weighed exactly the same as the piece of gold from which it was supposed to have been made.

But the king was still afraid that he had been tricked. The next day he called Archimedes to his palace. Archimedes was the wisest man in all his kingdom.

"Tell me, Archimedes," the king asked, "how can I be sure that all of my gold was put into the crown? How can I be sure that something of less worth has not been melted in with my fine gold?"

Not even Archimedes had an answer for such a problem. "Let me think about your question for a time," he replied. "Perhaps I can find an answer."

For several days the wise old man thought about the king's problem. There seemed to be no way to tell whether the crown was all of gold.

Then, early one morning, Archimedes went to take a bath. His careless servant had filled the tub to the very top. Without thinking, Archimedes stepped into the bathtub. Water poured over the edge and spilled onto the floor.

The wise old fellow saw that the water he had spilled took up the same space in the tub that was now filled by his body. A larger man would have spilled more water onto the floor. A smaller man than he would not have spilled as much!

Quickly Archimedes' mind began to work. Gold was more heavy than silver or anything else that might have been put into the king's crown. Anything except gold would take up more space than gold.

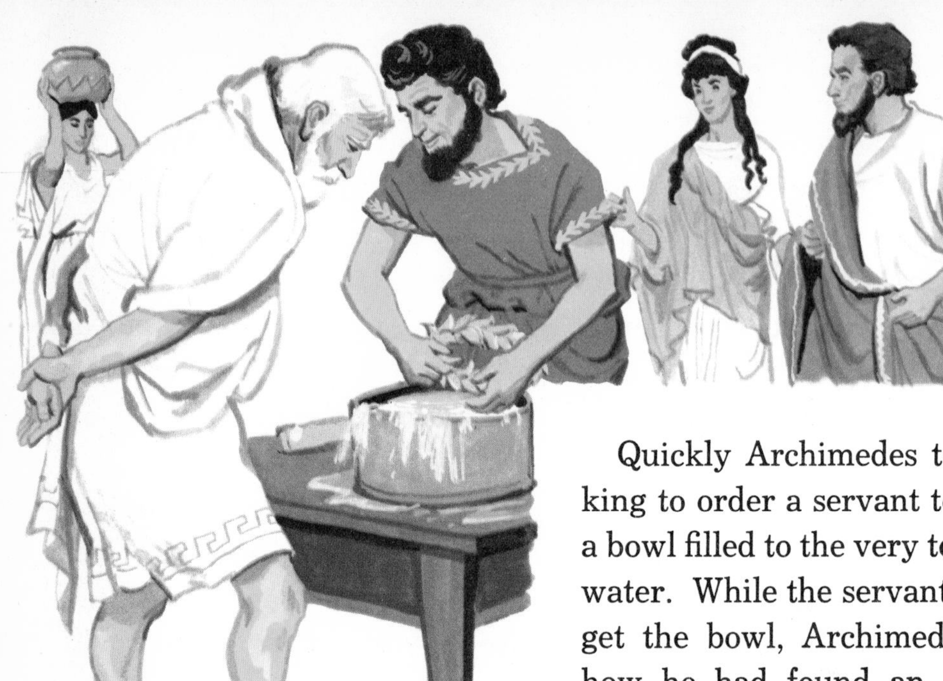

Why not put the crown in a bowl full of water! If it were not all made of gold it would take up more space than would gold.

"Eureka! I have found it! I have found the answer!" Archimedes cried. Without even waiting to put on his clothes he jumped out of the tub and ran down the street towards the king's palace. He burst into the room where the king sat. A few drops of water fell to the palace floor.

Quickly Archimedes told the king to order a servant to bring a bowl filled to the very top with water. While the servant ran to get the bowl, Archimedes told how he had found an answer to the king's problem. He explained that if the crown were not all made of gold it would make more water spill over the side than would a piece of gold of the same weight. "Anything less heavy than gold will take up more space if it weighs as much as the gold does," he said.

When a bowl of water was put on the table, the king first placed a piece of gold in it. The gold weighed the same as the crown. Only a little water spilled over the edge of the bowl.

Then the bowl was again filled to the top. Slowly the king placed his new crown in the water. Much more water spilled over the edge and spread across the table! "This is exactly what I thought," cried the king. "I was tricked! That man kept part of my gold for himself when he made the crown. I will get the gold back and see that he is beaten for trying to steal it."

Once again people told one another how great and wise was Archimedes. Once again the people of Greece said that he probably was the wisest man in the world.

They were quite right. Even today many of the things that Archimedes learned and told others have been of great use to men everywhere.

To this very day people sometimes say "Eureka" when they learn something important. Eureka is the Greek word for "I have found it!" which Archimedes used as he sat in his tub watching water pour onto the floor.

Wonders of Words

"Eureka!" shouted wise Archimedes when he made his great discovery. What an exciting story the word tells.

There are stories about words just as there are stories about fairies and battles, and kings and queens. Listen to the interesting tales of some other words you know.

Volcano is called after the Roman god, *Vulcan*. He was the son of Jupiter and god of fire. His workroom was inside the top of a very high mountain where he made armor for all the gods. To make the armor, he kept very hot fires burning inside the mountain.

One day Vulcan took the part of the queen of gods and goddesses against Jupiter. The lord of gods became so angry he threw Vulcan off the top of the mountain. Vulcan was nine days in falling. At last he was picked up by fishermen. He was half dead and his leg was broken.

That is how a mountain which throws out fire and lava came to be called a volcano, after Vulcan.

Do you know why twelve inches is called a *foot*? Most boys and girls can tell you a foot is twelve inches. But do you know how that came to be?

Long, long ago, a foot was the distance from a man's heel to his toe. On every man it was different. Sometimes a foot was ten inches, and sometimes more. On a very large man, a foot might even be nineteen inches. Then some wise men, in the days of King Edward II of England, in the year 1324, decided that hereafter a foot would be twelve inches.

Animal names have quite as interesting stories. *Mouse* means a thief, a stealer. This word comes to us from an old language which was used in India long, long ago. The name for this little animal was *mush* which meant "to steal."

Of course you cannot learn the story of every word in the world. But if you try you can find exciting adventures hidden in the stories of many words.

Old Sayings About the Weather

When the grass is dry at night,
Look for rain before the light.

When the grass is dry at morning light,
Look for rain before the night.

A deep, clear sky of cloudless blue
Brings storms within a day or two.

. . . . .

When the wind is in the east,
It's good for neither man nor beast.

When the wind is in the north,
The old folk should not travel forth.

When the wind is in the south,
It blows the worms in the fish's mouth.

When the wind is in the west,
It is of all the winds the best.

. . . . .

Evening red and morning gray
Sends the traveler on his way.

Evening gray and morning red
Sends the traveler home to bed.

FROM A SHEPHERD'S HANDS

Keep yourself clean and bright;
you are the window through
which you must see the world.

George Bernard Shaw

The Little Shepherd's Song

The leaves, the little birds, and I,
The white clouds and the sweet, sweet sky,
The pages singing as they ride
Down there, down there where the river is wide—
Heigh-ho, what a day! What a lovely day!
Even too lovely to hop and play
With my sheep
Or sleep
In the sun!

And so I lie in the deep, deep grass
And watch the pages as they pass,
And sing to them as they to me,
Till they turn the bend by the big old tree.
And then—Oh then, I sing right on
To the leaves and the lambs and myself alone!
For I think there must be
Inside of me
A bird!

William Alexander Percy

How Pierre Helped to Build a Cathedral

A few years ago I was taking a trip through France. I came to a small city in which there was a great cathedral.

Just as the sun was going down I went into the grand old place. At one side was a huge and wonderful window made of many pieces of colored glass. As the setting sun shone through the window, I said aloud, "In all my life I have never seen anything so lovely!"

An old man was standing at my shoulder. He heard me speak and said, "Would you like to hear an old, old tale about that great window?"

I asked the old man to have supper with me. After we ate in a little place near the railroad station, we had coffee in a small garden. While we sat there in the growing darkness he told me this story.

Our great cathedral was built almost five hundred years ago. It might never have had that beautiful window if it had not been for a boy named Pierre.

Pierre was, perhaps, ten years old. He looked after his sheep in the fields near the town. He was very poor and his clothes were full of holes. In his home there often was not enough food for the family supper.

Now in the days of long ago when Pierre was a boy, people in many parts of France were building cathedrals. Often the half-finished towers reached up toward the sky for many years until the townspeople had enough money to do more work on them. Some of the cathedrals were not finished for three or four hundred years.

As he stood among the sheep, Pierre could often see his neighbors pulling wagons with huge pieces of rock to the town. Once in the town the rocks would be cut and shaped. At last they would be fitted together to make the thick walls of the cathedral. The people themselves pulled the wagons and everyone helped. Even the great duke who lived in a castle took his turn at the ropes.

With all his heart, Pierre wished that he could do something to help build the big cathedral. But there seemed to be nothing that he could do. Nothing, at least, until he was older. Perhaps then he could help to pull the heavy rocks.

Late one day in summer a long line of men were pulling a loaded wagon to the cathedral. They stopped near where Pierre was watching his sheep. They had decided to make camp for the night.

After supper, while his sheep were sleeping, Pierre came over to talk to the men. Suddenly in the nearby woods they heard the cries of a band of wolves.

As the cries came nearer, the men decided to have the fun of a wolf chase. They took pieces of burning wood from the fire and ran off to frighten the wolves. With luck they might even kill one of the animals and have its hide to sell.

With wolves nearby in the neighborhood, Pierre hurried back to his sheep. He threw more logs on the fire around which the sheep, in great fear, were trembling. No wolf dared come near a good fire and the boy felt quite safe as he looked at his sheep.

Pierre could hear the men and older boys chasing the wolves through the woods. It sounded as if they were having a wonderful time.

Then the cries of the hunters changed. They sounded frightened. Something must have gone wrong.

Suddenly a man burst from the woods. Pierre could see him clearly in the light of the full moon. A great wolf ran snapping at his heels.

In a few seconds other men came running from the woods. They waved their burning sticks and bravely tried to turn the wolf away from their friend.

Then Pierre realized what was wrong. The great beast was mad! A mad wolf! His bite would kill any man in whom he dug his teeth. No wonder the men feared him.

Almost without thinking, Pierre pulled off his long coat. He ran between the man and the mad animal. Quickly he threw the coat over the wolf's great head and fell upon him. Both beast and boy lay struggling on the earth.

"Kill him! Kill him quickly!" Pierre cried as the man ran up.

In a few seconds the wolf lay still with a huge knife in his heart.

"This wolf's hide will be yours!" a big man told Pierre. "You can sell the hide for a piece of silver."

"No," said Pierre. "You sell the wolf hide. Let the silver money be used to help pay for a great colored-glass window for the cathedral. Perhaps it will buy one little piece of glass."

The old Frenchman who was telling me the story of Pierre stopped. I thought that he had come to the end of his tale. "And was that how Pierre helped to build the cathedral?" I asked.

The old man smiled kindly. "But no!" he said. "That is only part of the story.

"The man whose life Pierre saved had come to the town to make the great window for the cathedral. If Pierre had not stopped the great beast the man would not have lived to make the wonderful glass.

"So you see, in a way, this great window is a gift to men today from the hands of a brave boy who watched his sheep in these fields five hundred years ago."

Gifts for the Gods

Long years ago, a wild, fierce people lived among the woods and hills of Northern Europe. They believed that many strange gods ruled their lives. On the long, cold winter nights they told strange tales of their gods and their mysterious adventures.

Here is a story to which children listened more than a thousand years ago as they sat near the fires in their homes.

Of all the gods of the cold Northland there was none as mean and unkind as Loki, the red-haired fire-god. None of the other gods liked the tricks he played on them. But they were never so angry with him as they were when he stole the golden hair from the head of Thor's lovely wife.

Thor was away from home one day and his wife lay sleeping in their palace garden. Loki was walking past. Being a nosey fellow, he peeked in the garden gate. He saw that Thor's wife was sound asleep with the sunlight playing on her beautiful hair.

Quickly Loki went through the gate. He drew his long, sharp knife and walked over to the sleeping woman. He cut the beautiful golden hair from her head. Then he hurried off, laughing at his mean trick.

When Thor's wife woke and opened her eyes, her head felt strangely light. She raised her hand to her head. After a second or two, she burst into tears. "My hair," she cried, "my lovely hair is gone!"

When Thor came home later in the day he found the poor woman hiding and weeping in a little room in the palace. She was ashamed to have the other gods, or even her husband, see her bare head.

"Your golden hair is gone!" cried Thor. "There is nothing left on your head but soft down like that on a baby bird." His poor wife could not answer, but only sat blinded by her tears.

Thor grew so angry that it was frightening to see his face. "Loki!" he cried. "Only Loki would do such a thing!" He hurried after the fire-god and at last caught up with him.

"Loki," cried Thor, "how could you steal my wife's golden hair? You must get more hair for her!"

For once in his life, Loki was really very frightened. "I promise!" he said when he had got his breath. "I promise to bring your wife some golden hair if only you will let me go."

Thor took his hands from Loki and let him go free. Thor knew that even Loki would have to keep his word because a god could not break a promise.

The job of finding new golden hair for Thor's wife was not as difficult for Loki as you might think. The fire-god knew where the wee dwarfs lived far under the earth. He also knew that they could make almost anything in their magic workshops.

Loki went down to the dark underground world of the dwarfs which lay beneath some great mountains. When the wee dwarfs heard what the fire-god wanted, they at once set to work. From their softest gold they made long, thin threads. They were as fine as the hair which Loki had cut from the head of Thor's wife. The dwarfs told him that the golden hair would grow on her head when Loki put it there.

The fire-god knew that all the gods were angry because of his many poor tricks and bad jokes. He decided to take along some other gifts for them, too.

"I have never seen anything so fine as this golden hair!" he then declared. "Do you think that you could make two more beautiful gifts for me? I would like to give one to the king of the gods and one to the sun-god."

The dwarfs were pleased by Loki's honeyed words and at once went back to work. The very next day they gave the fire-god a magic arrow and a magic ship so small that it would fit into one's pocket.

"The golden arrow will always hit its mark when the king of the gods shoots it," the dwarfs told Loki. "The little silver ship will grow bigger and bigger when the sun-god puts it on the water," they said. "It will carry forty men and it will travel wherever he wishes, even when there is no wind to blow it."

Loki thanked the dwarfs warmly, as well he might. Then he started for the city of the gods. On his way out of the dwarfs' caves he met one of the little men whose name was Truck.

Now the fire-god liked to talk. He told Truck that some of the other dwarfs had made him the very best gifts in the world.

Truck laughed at Loki's proud words. "Your presents are not so fine, oh, fire-god," he said. "Why, my brother, Rock, could make three gifts that would be even more pleasing to the gods than the three you now carry!"

"Listen to me, my little friend," said Loki, "if your brother can make three presents that are better than mine you may cut off my head. But if your gifts do not please the gods more than mine do, then I will cut off your head!" The dwarf agreed and hurried away.

Truck ran to his brother's cave and told him the story. "Have no fear," said Rock. "We will win. Loki will lose his head."

First, Rock built a fire in his workshop. Then he put a piece of leather in the flames. "Now I must go out," he said to Truck. "Be sure to blow upon the fire every second that I am away. If you do not keep blowing, the magic gift may not turn out right."

Loki was sure that he would win, but he decided to take no chances. He changed himself into a huge horsefly. Then he flew into the cave where Truck was working at the fire. Around and around flew Loki. Then he settled on the dwarf's hand and bit him.

When the horsefly bit Truck it felt as if someone had run a hot needle into his hand. But he did not stop blowing upon the fire.

When Rock returned he took a beautiful little golden pig from the fire. Then he threw a piece of fine gold on the hot flames. Again he told Truck not to stop blowing upon the fire for even one second, and went away.

No sooner had Rock gone than Loki returned in the shape of a horsefly. This time the fly landed on Truck's neck. The dwarf cried out when he felt the needle-like bite, but he kept on blowing.

In a few minutes Rock came back. This time he took a heavy golden ring from the fire and put a large piece of iron in the flames. Once more he warned Truck to keep blowing while he was gone.

The third time that Loki flew into the cave he settled between poor Truck's eyes and bit him just as fiercely as he could.

This time the little dwarf stopped blowing on the fire and drove the horsefly away from his face. When Rock returned and heard what Truck had done, he was very angry. "The third gift may not be any good at all," he cried. "I'm almost afraid to take the iron from the fire." However, the third gift, a heavy hammer, appeared to be all right.

Rock told Truck of the magic powers of each of the gifts. Then he sent his brother on his way to the city of the gods. Loki met the dwarf in front of the palace of the king of the gods. Together they went inside to see whose gifts would be more pleasing to the gods, who were waiting in the palace.

Loki gave the golden arrow to the king of the gods and explained that it always hit its mark. Then the dwarf handed the gold ring to the king, saying, "Each night a second ring exactly like the first will drop from it." The king of the gods thought for a moment. Then he declared, "The dwarf's gift pleases me more than does Loki's arrow."

Next Loki gave the small silver ship to the sun-god. "You can carry it in your pocket," Loki explained, "but when you put it on the water it grows big enough to hold forty men." The sun-god was very happy to receive a present that was so beautiful.

Then Truck stepped up and gave the sun-god the gold pig.

"If you set him on the ground," said the dwarf, "the pig becomes as large as a horse and will fly through the air with you on his back." The sun-god looked at both gifts. At last he said that he liked the flying pig more than he liked the magic boat.

Loki still hoped that his last gift, the golden hair, would be more pleasing to Thor than the dwarf's iron hammer. The fire-god stepped up to Thor's wife and placed the hair on her head.

The golden hair took root and began to grow on her head as if it were her own! It was even more beautiful than the hair Loki had cut from her head.

Great Thor cried out with pleasure! He at once forgave Loki for stealing his wife's hair while she slept in the garden.

When the dwarf gave Thor the iron hammer, the god did not seem to like it. He looked at his wife's golden hair, then at the ugly hammer. It was easy to see which gift he thought was the better one.

"Wait! Let me speak before you decide which is the better gift," cried the dwarf. "This hammer is so strong that it will break a mountain in two. Nothing can stand before it, and it will always return to your hand after you throw it."

"Truck wins!" cried the gods, and Thor had to agree that the dwarf had, indeed, won.

"Now where is Loki?" asked Truck. "Let me cut off his head!"

But Loki had seen that he had lost. He had run off, and it was a long time before he came back to make more trouble for the gods.

Gifts from the Gods

Have you ever thought about the days of the week, and how they got their names? Do you know that the name of each day is a gift from a god or goddess? The story is an old, old tale. It is as old as the stories of the gods and goddesses who were thought to rule the world.

Ages ago men prayed to the sun. They knew that the sun was great. It gave the people light and warmth. Without it nothing could grow. So they named the first day *Sun Day* for the great sun-god.

Monday is really *Moon Day*. People loved the goddess of the moon because she was gentle and beautiful. Boys and girls loved her very much. On her feast day children made little round cakes with candles all around them.

Tuesday is named for the god of war. A terrible wolf was troubling the whole earth. No one was brave enough to catch him. So the god of war set out on this dangerous trip. He had the dwarfs of the mountains make him a chain out of the hardest things in the world to find. In the chain he had the footsteps of a cat, the hair of women, the roots of stones, and the breath of fishes. With the chain he caught the terrible wolf. It is from this brave god that Tuesday got its name.

The king of the gods gave *Wednesday* its name. He lived in a palace built of silver and gold. On his shoulders were two big black birds. When he wanted to know what was going on in the world, he sent one of the black birds to find out. Each day the birds flew all around the world and brought him news of everything that was happening.

Thursday is named for Thor, the mighty god about whom you have read. He was the strongest of all the gods of the North. He could break a mountain in two with the magic hammer the dwarf gave him. But there were a few things he could not do. One time he tried to drink all the water that was in a horn. But the more he drank, the more it filled up. For, you see, the other end of the horn was in the sea. Because Thor was so great, people began to say, "If you have any hard work to do, start it on Thor's Day."

The day for music, flowers, and elves is *Friday*. The goddess for whom this day is named ruled the rain and sunshine, and all the fruits of the earth. When the goddess was sad, her tears came down as raindrops, and when she was happy, the sun shone. Some people thought that because she cried a lot, Friday was an unhappy day. And today you may still hear some folks say that Friday is a day for bad luck.

Saturday is a day for fun and feast. Some folks said that the Roman god for whom this day was named ate his own children. He was afraid of each child. But others liked him very much. He ruled during a time that was called the Golden Age. Because he was such a good ruler, a feast was held in the wintertime every year. On that day no one worked. Friends gave presents to each other. And masters would make fine feasts for their servants. Thus Saturday became one of the pleasantest days of the week.

If you would like to read more about gifts from the gods, look for other stories about these mighty rulers.

EXPLORERS BOLD

Where lies the land to which the ship would go?
Far, far ahead, is all explorers know.
And where the land she travels from? Away,
Far, far behind, is all that they can say.

Arthur Hugh Clough

EUROPE
ASIA
GENOA
VENICE
MEDITERRANEAN SEA
JERUSALEM
ARABIA
TIBET
CHINA
PEKING
JAPAN
INDIA
PACIFIC OCEAN
ARABIAN SEA
EAST INDIES
AFRICA
INDIAN OCEAN
SUMATRA

Marco Polo Comes Home

Marco Polo was a boy who lived in Venice, a beautiful city in Europe. He lived seven hundred years ago and had many wonderful adventures. When he was about eleven years old, Marco set out on a great journey with his father and his uncle. These men were merchants who made their living by buying and selling goods.

With Marco, they traveled all the way to China. This was a wonderful and brave thing to do in those days. As far as we know, the Polos were the first merchants to make the dangerous trip from Europe to China.

For ten long years the Polo family bought and sold goods in China. By the time Marco Polo had become a man, his father and his uncle were very rich. Even the great Emperor of China was their friend.

At last the Polos wanted to return to their home in Venice. But the Emperor would not hear of it! He wanted Marco Polo to help him run his great kingdom. So it was that ten more years passed.

When the Chinese Emperor was an old, old man, he called Marco to his side. He said that Marco, his father, and his uncle could return to Europe at last. "You have been of great help to me," the Emperor told him. "But I will keep you here no longer. I know you want to return to your own people."

The Emperor gave the Polos many rich gifts and sent them on their way. The three men once again journeyed far across the face of the earth. At last, in the year 1289, they returned to their home in Venice.

After all the years that had gone by, the three Polos could not even find their house. They had to ask people to show them the way to their street. When they came to their home, the servant who came to the door did not know them! He did not want to let them come in and Marco had to push his way through the door.

The neighbors, as they looked from their windows, said, "These cannot be the Polos. They are strangers!"

The next day Marco and his father and his uncle had a long talk. They decided to give a great dinner to show their old friends and neighbors that they really were the Polo family.

Plans were made for the feast, and everyone who was invited said he would come. Indeed, the whole city of Venice was talking about the three men who said they were the Polos. Few people believed the story that they really had been to faraway China. But everyone wanted to hear what they had to say. Even the great Duke who ruled the city of Venice planned to come.

On the night of the feast, the Polos dressed themselves in brightly colored Chinese clothes and met the friends whom they had asked to dinner.

The Polos' visitors were not very friendly! Most of them were quite sure that the dinner would turn out to be a huge joke. At the same time, nothing could have kept them from coming to see what would happen!

When the fine dinner had ended, Marco Polo got to his feet. "Good friends and good neighbors," he said, "in China, after a great feast, the Emperor has music or dancing for his friends. Sometimes there is play acting or singing.

"But tonight," Marco went on, "we thought that you might like to see some of the riches of faraway China!"

Then the three Polos went into the next room. Quickly they changed into the old and dirty clothes which they wore when they had arrived in Venice. Dressed in these poor clothes they walked in and stood before their friends.

The great Duke of Venice got to his feet. He looked angry. "What kind of bad joke is this?" he cried. "Are these dirty clothes the things we have come to see?"

Marco Polo smiled. "Give us one minute, mighty Duke," he said. Then, with these words, he and the older Polos took knives and cut open the travel-worn clothes.

When their friends and neighbors saw the jewels the Polos had hidden in their old clothes, they were sure that the Polos' story was true. The great Duke told Marco that the city of Venice was pleased to have the Polo family safely home with their riches!

When the last of their friends had gone, the Polos knew that their surprise party had been a fine one! The Duke had asked them to come to his palace for dinner! Everyone now believed that they had really been to China.

"Well!" said Marco with a laugh, "the people of Venice may not have believed that our story was true when we looked like poor travelers. But everyone believes a story when the men who tell it have a mountain of jewels!"

Moon Magic

Columbus knew many things about sailing ships. He knew about the moon and stars, too.

One time Columbus learned something about the moon that saved his life, and the lives of his men, too. Study the picture on this page and read what Columbus found out.

This is what Columbus knew about the moon:

1. The moon does not have light of its own.
2. You can see the moon only when the sun's light is on it.
3. Sometimes the earth comes between the moon and the sun. When the sun, earth, and moon are all in the same line, the earth cuts off the light from the sun. Then the moon is in the shadow of the earth and cannot be seen. When this happens the moon is *eclipsed* or hidden. In a few hours the moon moves out of the shadow of the earth and is bright once again.

In the picture **S** is the sun,
E is the earth,
M is the moon.

On February 28, 1504, Columbus was worried because the Indians were no longer friendly. He picked up a book which he had brought with him and began to read. He read that on the very next night there would be an eclipse of the moon. That gave Columbus an idea.

As you read the exciting story about "Columbus and the Eclipse," see if you can tell how he used what he learned to make "moon magic."

Columbus and the Eclipse

Almost everyone knows the story of how Columbus came across the great ocean in 1492 with his three small ships. Not many people, however, know how the sun and the moon helped Columbus when he had trouble with the Indians.

A few years after Columbus had come to the New World, he and about fifty of his men were living in a small town they had built. The town was on one of the islands which Columbus had discovered.

When Columbus and his men had first come to the island, the Indians had been friendly. They had thought that the white men were gods who had come across the great ocean.

For several months the Indians had brought goods to trade with the soldiers and food for them to eat. But as time passed the Indians decided that the white men were not gods. The magic of their guns no longer seemed mysterious. They became ill just as the Indians did. An arrow could kill them unless they wore their strange iron clothes. Soon the Indians became less friendly.

At last the Indians no longer came with gifts and food. They no longer brought bits of gold to trade for little bells or red cloth. Columbus knew that he must do something to show the Indians that the white man's magic was strong.

It happened that Columbus had brought an important book with him on his ship. The book told him that there soon would be an eclipse of the moon.

As Columbus read his book, he had an idea. He sent some of his soldiers to bring the Indian chief before him.

When the Indian chief had arrived Columbus told him that he must bring food for the soldiers as he had promised. He also told the chief to bring goods to trade.

The chief looked angry. He shook his head and said that his people would do no more work, nor would they bring food. "You have no magic," he said to Columbus. "The white men are no gods. They are men just like the Indians."

"Now hear me," Columbus said. "The white man has great magic. If you do not believe me, come here tonight. I will take the round silver moon from the sky if you do not keep your promise to bring food for my soldiers!"

In his heart the Indian leader was a little afraid, but he said, "You cannot take the moon away. Tonight I will bring all my people here. They will see that what you say is not true. They will see that the white man has no magic."

That night, as the great silver moon came up, hundreds of Indians came to sit in the open fields near the little town. They were very quiet. Many of them really were afraid that Columbus would hide the moon.

How Columbus must have hoped that his book was right!

It would be a great blow to his plans if there were no eclipse of the moon. Never again would the Indians believe him.

The Indians grew restless. At last the chief got to his feet. He walked over to Columbus. "The moon is still bright in the sky!" he laughed. "Where is your magic?"

"Look!" said Columbus, pointing up at the moon.

One edge of the moon had disappeared! As the minutes passed the black shadow spread.

The Indian leader and his people cried out in fear. They ran off in every direction. Soon they were streaming back with food in their hands.

The Indians then lay on the earth covering their faces in fear of Columbus. The old chief, in words that trembled, asked him to bring back the silver moon. Columbus promised to do so if the Indians agreed to bring food each day.

The eclipse passed at last and once again the moon shone bright and clear. The Indian chief kept his word. After that Columbus and all his men had all the food they wanted to eat.

The Explorer

He listened, quiet in his seat, and how, then, did I know
That one boy, right before my eyes, a-traveling would go.
And if you would travel with him in explorations bold,
Search all the lines and spaces for great adventures of old.

What can you find in the picture below?

STORIES YOU'LL LIKE

One gift the Fairies gave me—
The love of Book, the Golden Key
That opens the Magic Door.

Andrew Lang

Riddle Me Ree

Riddle me, riddle me, riddle me ree,
If you know the answers, a wise man you'll be.

● I have a little sister, they call her Peep, Peep;
She goes through waters deep, deep, deep;
She climbs the mountains high, high, high;
Poor little thing, she has but one eye.
Tell me this riddle if you can.

● ● Formed long ago, yet made today,
I'm most in use when others sleep;
What few would like to give away,
And none would like to keep.
What am I?

● ● ● What is that which no man ever yet did see,
Which never was, but always is to be?

● ● ● ● I am, as you'll agree with me,
The funniest thing in land or sea.
My mouth is bigger than my head,
I always stay within my bed.
What am I?

Answers to the riddles of long ago
Are on page 237, if you don't know.

How the Swiss Family Robinson Saved Its Cattle

Many years ago a family named Robinson lived in Switzerland. They decided to come to the New World to make their home.

For many weeks they traveled to the west over the ocean. At last, when they were just a few days away from the New World, a great wind began to blow. The sky grew black and huge waves poured over the little ship which carried them. For two days the captain could not even steer his ship. The ship went wherever the wind and the big waves took her.

At last the ship was blown near an island. There were sharp rocks in the water near the shore, and the ship struck them with a crash!

"The ship is going down!" the captain cried. The few men who were left ran to the small lifeboat and put it over the side. They jumped in quickly while the captain ran to call Mr. Robinson, his wife, and their four sons.

As bad luck would have it, a great wall of water came over the side of the ship and, when it was gone, so was the poor captain. He had been carried away by the huge wave.

In great fear, then, the men pushed off from the ship. They were afraid that if they waited to get the Robinson family they, too, would be killed. But no sooner had they pulled away from the ship than another great wave turned their small boat over. In less than a minute there was not one of the men's heads to be seen above the black water.

When the ship had hit the great rock, the six Robinsons were safe inside her. No one came to call them. They thought perhaps that all the men were too hard at work to tell them what had happened.

Mr. Robinson, his wife, and his sons were afraid, too.

After some time had passed the wind became less noisy and the angry waves seemed less fierce. At last Mr. Robinson went above to see what had happened. He came back quickly to tell the family that they had been left behind and were alone on the ship.

"There is an island near us," he went on to say. "We may be able to reach land when the water is more smooth."

There was no boat to carry the family to the island. But Mr. Robinson and Fritz, his oldest son, found some empty barrels. In a few hours they had used the barrels to make a strong raft. The wind had stopped blowing, so they put the raft over the side of the ship.

The family loaded the raft with many things they would need, such as tools, garden seeds, food, guns, knives, and warm clothes. They also brought along their two big dogs. When everyone was on the raft, Fritz and Mr. Robinson pushed off for the island which was about a half mile away.

The first night the Robinsons slept under the stars. The four boys thought it was great fun, like being on a camping trip.

After breakfast Mr. Robinson held up his long spyglass and looked out at the ship. Mrs. Robinson and their sons stood at his side.

"Our ship seems to be caught fast on that great sharp rock," he said at last. "But we have no time to waste! We must bring everything we can to the island. We must bring it here at once. Soon the wind and water will break her to pieces."

"But why must we do all that work?" cried the smallest boy. "We will not need much for the few weeks we will be here."

Almost sadly Mr. Robinson looked at his family for a moment. At last he said with a brave smile, "We may need everything on that ship. It could be fifty years before anyone comes to our island."

Mrs. Robinson spoke up quickly, as if to hide the fear that no one would ever find them. "What will we get first?" she asked.

"First we must get the cattle from the bottom hold in the ship," Mr. Robinson said. "If they are still alive we should have two cows, four pigs, three goats, and two sheep."

Only Mr. Robinson and big Fritz went out to the ship. They needed every bit of room there was on the raft to carry goods to shore. "The raft is too small to hold the cattle," said Fritz. "How will we get them to the shore of the island?" he asked.

"I have been thinking about that," his father told him. "Do you have any ideas, son? We need those cows."

"Could we tie each of the animals between two barrels?" asked Fritz. "We might be able to pull them to shore that way!"

"A good plan, a very good idea," said Mr. Robinson. "Let's try it. But we must keep our guns ready. There may be sharks in these waters!"

When they reached the ship, Mr. Robinson and Fritz were happy to find the cattle alive and well, but very hungry.

After they had fed the cattle, they looked around and found some empty water barrels. With Fritz helping, Mr. Robinson used cloth and rope to tie a barrel on each side of a sheep. When they pushed the beast into the water he rode the waves beautifully.

Quickly they fastened barrels to the other ten animals. Then they loaded the raft with more tools and food and made ready to go back to the island.

Sure enough! A long, black shadow was sliding through the water. As Fritz and his father watched, the shark turned part way on one side and headed for one of the three goats. They could see his great white teeth and open mouth as the huge fish closed in on the helpless goat.

All went well until Mr. Robinson and Fritz were about a thousand yards from shore. "Look!" cried Fritz. "Look! Isn't that huge fish a shark?"

Only for a second did Fritz sit still. Then the boy reached for his gun. He fired just as the shark's teeth were about to snap shut on the goat.

As the shot rang out there was a great splash and the shark disappeared. There was only a red streak on the water to show where he had been.

The next few minutes were wild ones. More and more sharks appeared. Fritz and Mr. Robinson fired their guns as fast as they could load them.

Luckily, the light wind soon carried the raft down toward the shore. Also, the sharks stopped and ate one of the other sharks which had been killed. This gave Fritz and Mr. Robinson the time they needed to pull for the island.

At last the water in which the raft floated was not deep enough for the sharks to follow it. The cattle had been saved!

The Swiss family Robinson carried most of the goods from the ship before it slid off the rock and disappeared under the ocean. Then they cleared land for a farm. They lived for over ten years on their island which they had come to call Little Switzerland.

At last a ship from England found the Robinsons. The boys went off to school in Europe but came back later. Mr. and Mrs. Robinson loved the island so much that they stayed there all their lives. Little Switzerland had become their home and they could not bear to leave it.

How Arthur Became King of England

It was a cold, dark night in England of long ago. An old man hurried along a road through the deep woods. The man was Merlin, a wise man and a magician.

As he walked, Merlin asked himself, "Why is it that the king has ordered me to come to his castle at such a late hour? Something must have happened."

Merlin made his way to a small door in the castle wall. He knocked on the door softly. A soldier had been waiting for him. He opened the door and told the magician to come in.

The old soldier led Merlin to a small room where they found the king.

"I thank you for coming so quickly, my friend," the king said. "Now listen carefully to my words. A son was born tonight to my wife, the queen. He is our first and only child."

Merlin started to tell the king how pleased he was to hear the good news. But the king signaled him to be quiet and went on speaking.

"I have given my son the name of Arthur," said the king. "And I have called you here so that he will have a better chance to become the king when I am gone."

"What do you mean? What can I do?" asked Merlin.

"I am an old man," said the king. "I probably will not live long enough to see Arthur grow to be a man. One of the dukes or princes in my kingdom may try to kill little Arthur and steal the crown for himself," the king went on.

"This very night I will give the child to you. Take him and find a good home for him. Tell no one that he is my son. Then, when Arthur is old enough, see that he is crowned King of England."

Merlin promised to do as the king asked. Then, sadly, the king went into the next room. He came back with Arthur, and gave him to Merlin.

The magician took the child, and the old soldier let him out of the castle through the little door in the great wall. The next day Merlin took Arthur to the home of a kindly duke who had a baby son of his own named Kay. Merlin asked the duke to bring up Arthur as if he were Kay's own brother.

The duke agreed to take care of Arthur as Merlin asked. So it was that Arthur and Kay grew up in the duke's castle believing that they were really brothers.

The years passed quickly. Arthur and Kay learned to use the sword, and to shoot an arrow straight to its mark. They hunted deer in the duke's great woods and they chased rabbits across the fields near his castle. The two boys grew tall and strong, and no one but the duke knew that Arthur was not his true son.

When Arthur was almost grown to be a man, the old king, his true father, was killed in a war. At once many of the dukes and princes wanted to be king of England in his place.

Old Merlin called all of the leaders in the kingdom together on Christmas. For a long time they tried to decide who would be king. They could not agree, but promised to meet again the next day.

As the men left the great cathedral to which Merlin had called them, a strange sight met their eyes. In front of the cathedral was a huge rock that had not been there before. Stuck in the rock was a beautiful magic sword. On the sword these words appeared:

Who so ever can pull me free,
That man England's king
will be.

At once all the dukes and princes who wanted to be king agreed that the man who could pull the sword from the rock would be their ruler. Then they took turns trying to pull the sword free.

But try as they might, no man was able to move the great sword so much as an inch! They all tried until their faces turned red, but the sword stayed in the rock.

The news of the magic sword spread. Men came from all over the kingdom hoping to draw the sword. Each thought that he might become king, but every man failed. Months went by and the sword remained stuck fast.

The winter passed and the world welcomed the spring with its flowers and green grass. There was a great feast planned in the city where the cathedral stood.

The duke brought Kay and Arthur to the city. As the three walked past the beautiful cathedral, Kay said, "I have forgotten my sword! It must be back at the inn where we slept last night."

"Let me get it for you," Arthur said, and turned to go back to the inn. Just then Arthur saw the great sword in the rock. Of course he had heard of the sword, as had everyone in the kingdom.

As a joke, Arthur called out to Kay, "Why should I run all the way back to the inn! Here is a sword for you."

With a laugh, Arthur ran over to the rock and took hold of the sword. Kay and the duke laughed, too! "Pull hard," they called. "Bigger men than you have tried to draw it forth!"

Suddenly Kay and his father were no longer laughing. They stood with their mouths open in surprise! Arthur had drawn the sword from the rock!

Everyone passing by turned to look at Arthur, standing sword in hand and just as surprised as anyone else. The great square in front of the cathedral grew strangely quiet. It was hard to believe that the sword had at last been pulled free. Then someone cried, "Long live the King!"

"Father," Arthur said at last, "how can this be? What does it mean?"

"Come back to the inn, my boy," the old duke said. "I will call my old friend, Merlin. He and I have many things to tell you, but only Merlin knows the whole story."

The old magician came just as soon as he heard the news. He told Arthur how the old king had sent away the baby son he had loved so that no harm would come to him.

When Merlin had finished his tale, Arthur turned to the duke and to Kay. "Even if I am the true king," he said, "you will always be a father and a brother to me."

The next day Merlin invited all the princes and dukes of the kingdom to come to the cathedral to crown Arthur the true king of England. In a week's time they had come from every corner of the land.

When they were all together in the cathedral, Merlin told the people the story. He told of how the old king had given the baby Arthur into his care.

"How do we know this tale of yours is a true one?" cried one of the dukes.

"Let us put the sword back into the rock," said Merlin. "Let us see if there be one among you who can draw out the sword. Then let us see again if Arthur can pull it from the rock."

The leaders of the kingdom agreed with the magician's plan to show that Arthur was the one who should be king. Merlin asked Arthur to give him the sword. Then, with the dukes and princes at his heels he went into the square in front of the cathedral.

Once again Merlin put the sword in the rock. Again many men tried to pull it out. When no one was able to move the huge sword, Merlin turned to Arthur. "Now it is your turn to try," he said.

Slowly Arthur moved up to the sword. He placed his hand upon it. Would he be able to pull it forth this time? Every eye was upon the boy as he stood there in the great square. Then, with an easy pull, the sword slipped out of the rock!

Every man fell to his knees. "Long live King Arthur!" they cried.

So it was that Arthur became King of England.

When Good King Arthur Ruled the Land

When good King Arthur ruled the land
He was a goodly king;
He used three barrels of corn meal
To make a bag pudding.

A large pudding the King did make,
And filled it well with fruit;
And in it put a lump of fat,
As big as his left boot.

The King and Queen did eat thereof,
And forty men beside;
And what they could not eat that night
The Queen next morning fried.

BEYOND THE SEA

The world is a great book,
of which they who never go from home
read only a page.

Augustine

The Sea

The Sea! The Sea! the open Sea!
The blue, the fresh, the ever free!
Without a mark, without a bound,
It runneth the earth's wide regions 'round;
It plays with clouds, it laughs at skies,
Or likes a sleeping creature lies.

I'm on the Sea! I'm on the Sea!
I am where I would ever be—
With the blue above, and the blue below,
And quiet wheresoe'er I go.
If a storm should come and awake the deep,
What matter? I shall ride and sleep.

(fragment) Harry Cornwall

The Boy Who Was Afraid

It happened many years ago, before the traders first came to the islands of the Pacific Ocean.

On one of the far Pacific islands there lived a boy who was called Mafatu. He was the *Boy Who Was Afraid*. The people of the islands loved brave boys and men. So Mafatu, because he was afraid, lived a most unhappy life.

Mafatu feared the ocean which lay all around him. When he was very little he had almost been killed when the wind and waves broke his small boat to pieces on the ocean. Only by good luck had he got to shore.

Now poor Mafatu trembled when he was out on the water.

The older people were not really unkind to Mafatu, but they had little use for him. It was the children who made him so very unhappy. The girls laughed at him and the boys did not invite him to play their games. Even Mafatu's father, the Chief, said that the boy was no good to anyone and put him to work making fish nets.

Mafatu's only real friend was a small dog. It followed him everywhere and the boy loved his dog dearly.

At last Mafatu could not bear to live on his father's island any longer. He decided to take his small boat and his dog and go across the ocean to another island. "If I run away now," Mafatu said to himself, "perhaps I can learn to be brave when I am on the ocean alone." So Mafatu took food and water, called his dog, and left the island in his boat before the sun came up the next morning.

Although he was still afraid of the water and trembled, the boy would not turn back. He and his dog traveled for many days through rain and wind or under the hot sun.

At last they came to a large island with mountains that climbed up to the sky. Here Mafatu made his lonely home. He made nets and caught fish to eat. He made himself tools and a strong knife. He even killed the fierce wild pigs that lived on the island. But in his heart Mafatu knew that he was ever afraid of the great ocean that spread about him on every side.

A large hammerhead shark lived near the island. He gave Mafatu much trouble because of the way he would tear the boy's nets and steal his fish.

One day Mafatu and his dog went out to the fish traps in his boat. As he was about to pull in a net, the shark swam to the surface and broke the fish trap with his big tail. Quickly he ate the fish that Mafatu had caught.

The boy was angry. But he was still too afraid to jump into the water and kill the shark with his knife.

Just then a big wave rolled the boat on its side. With a splash the boy's dog fell into the water!

Quickly the hammerhead shark shot through the water. The dog swam wildly for the boat, but Mafatu knew that the hammerhead would have him in his teeth in a second or two. His dog! His only real friend!

Without thinking, the boy put his knife between his teeth and jumped into the ocean. He came up under the shark and drove his knife deep, deep into the beast's soft, white underside!

The shark turned over and crashed into Mafatu. It seemed to be pushing him far down in the water. His ears rang and he needed air.

Then Mafatu pulled free. Up, up he came until his head popped out of the water. He climbed into his boat and pulled in his dog who still struggled in the waves.

The hammerhead, deep in the water below, was finished! Other sharks had come and were tearing him to pieces. Suddenly Mafatu realized what he had done. He had killed the shark to save his dog—and he had not been afraid!

But still the boy asked himself, "Am I really brave? Would I jump back into the water again? I cannot go back to my father's island until I am sure that I am no longer the *Boy Who Was Afraid*."

Several days went by and Mafatu could not decide whether he had lost his fear. Then, one morning, he and his dog made another trip out to the fish nets.

While Mafatu was pulling in the nets his fine knife fell into the ocean. Slowly it slipped down through the water until it lay on the sand at the bottom. The water was very clear and the boy could see the knife.

It had been difficult to make the knife and Mafatu did not want to lose it. But was he brave enough to go that far down in the blue-green water to get it? He must have it! But . . .

The water was forty feet deep. Even many men on his home island would not go that far under the surface. Was he still the *Boy Who Was Afraid?* "No!" Mafatu cried. "I will get my knife!"

He began to breathe deeply to get ready for the long trip to the bottom. Then with one last deep breath he went over the side of the boat.

Down, far down, went Mafatu. He felt the water grow colder. His heart pounded.

The world under the water seemed dark and dangerous. The strangely colored fish seemed to say, "Go back! Go back to the surface while you still can!"

The knife! There it lay on the sand on the bottom of the ocean. Mafatu took it in his hand. He began the long trip back to the warm sun and air above.

But in that second something like a long piece of hose darted out of a cave on the dark ocean floor. It caught the boy by his foot. Cold fear poured through Mafatu! It was a huge octopus!

The *Boy Who Was Afraid* found himself looking into the ugly face of the huge octopus.

Mafatu saw a fierce sea creature with cold eyes and a parrot mouth. Half-mad with fear he dug his sharp knife straight into one of the eyes that had stared at him. But the octopus kept its hold on him. It seemed to hold him even more tightly than before.

Blindly, Mafatu drove his knife into the other eye. He drove it into the octopus again and again.

Suddenly, after what seemed like hours, the sea beast let go its hold. Mafatu swam up, up toward light and air and life.

How far up the surface seemed! The boy's heart felt as though it would burst. He had to have air . . .

Then, just as he had given up hope, Mafatu's head came to the surface. He was right next to his boat. There he held on and took deep breaths of the life-giving air.

At last the boy felt strong enough to climb into the boat where his dog welcomed him with joy. He looked down into the water. There, forty feet below, was the octopus he had killed, a broken shadow on which the sharks were feeding.

He, Mafatu, was no longer the *Boy Who Was Afraid!* He had swum forty feet down into the ocean. He had killed the great octopus. He had carried his knife back to the surface.

Now he could go back to his father's island. Because he no longer feared the ocean, the boys and girls would never again make fun of him.

. . . . .

It happened many years ago, before the traders first came to the islands of the Pacific Ocean. The *Boy Who Was Afraid* lost his fear of the water and became a great man and a brave chief who was loved by his people.

Even today the people on the faraway Pacific island tell the story of Mafatu while they sit around their fires at night and the silver moon moves across the dark sky.

Surprises of the Seas

The Owl and the Pussy-Cat went to sea
In a beautiful pea-green boat.

from "The Owl and the Pussy-Cat"
Edward Lear

In small ships that seem as tiny as the one of the owl and the pussy-cat, brave men are adventuring on the mighty seas. They are finding many surprises.

Deep in the sea, men are discovering unknown rivers, mountains, and volcanoes. The world of the sea has many strange plants and animals. This is the world which Mafatu knew. Come along on an underwater trip and see some of the interesting creatures.

There is an octopus like the one that wrapped itself around Mafatu's leg. This animal is really quite interesting. Stories and moving pictures always show him as a huge, fierce creature. Nothing could be more wrong. He does not go after anything unless it threatens to harm him, or he wants food. Other times he tries to get away. He can change color quickly and can throw out a black cloud to hide his getaway. Mother octopus fastens her eggs in strings to rocky walls in the water. She never eats while she guards her eggs. When the young ones come out and swim away, she swims off and dies.

The shark that Mafatu killed was a dangerous one. Sharks are very dangerous when they are hungry. And who knows when they are hungry? So it is best to keep away from them. Yet men who explore the seas tell us that mostly sharks pay no attention to them. They hunt for food they can get more easily. And they must keep swimming all the time for that is the way sharks breathe.

Look at the beautiful living rainbows in the water! Here are some animals that look like flowers—lovely pinks and yellows. They are creatures with "feathers" of red, yellow, orange, brown, blue, or black.

What is even more strange, these "feathers" can see. On each "feather" is a tiny black dot which looks like an eye. The little animal uses his "feather eyes" to tell light and dark. With them he can tell when something is moving near him.

Here is a little worm. He can make himself look like a peanut when you pick him up. The peanut worm cannot tell the difference between sand and food, so he eats both. Some of these worms live to be fifty years old.

Perhaps you have seen a starfish before. He gets along well with his head in the middle. If you cut him in half you will soon have two whole starfishes.

Look at the beautiful small white shell-like creatures. No seaman likes them because they stick to the bottom of ships and must be cleaned off. These queer little animals stand on their heads and eat with their feet. They have "sliding doors" which they close when there is no water. This keeps them from drying up.

Listen carefully! Did you think the sea was a quiet place? Oh, no! The sea is a noisy place with fishes and other creatures making many sounds. Here is a strange little animal who can make a sound like a small drum. It is a sea horse. Father sea horse is very helpful because he takes care of his wife's eggs. He carries them in a little bag on the under side of his body until the baby sea horses come out of the eggs.

Yes, indeed! The world of the sea holds many surprises. Ocean explorers are busy making new discoveries and adventuring in the sea. Perhaps some day you, too, will make a great discovery about the oceans.

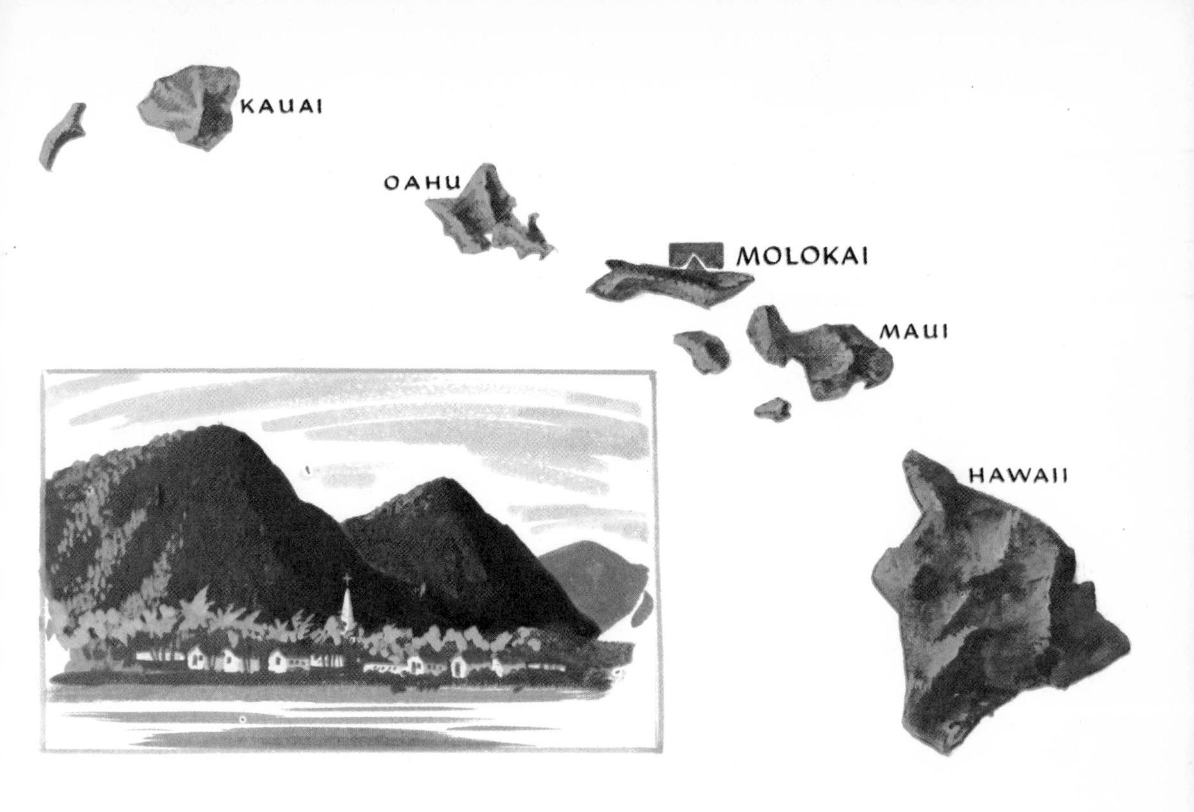

Father Damien's Gift

If you fly over the island of Molokai today, you can look out the airplane window. Below, you will see a clean, pleasant little city close to the edge of the Pacific Ocean. The blue-green water of the harbor and the dark green chain of high, jungle-covered hills back of the town make it appear very pretty and clean, indeed.

The town one sees on Molokai was not always the pleasant-looking place it is now. Once it was shut away from the rest of the world. People feared to go there. Here is the story of a great and good man. It is the story of how he made this unhappy corner of the earth a better place for the poor people who had to live there.

A hundred or more years ago people everywhere were very afraid of a sickness known as leprosy. In the Hawaiian Islands, men, women, and even children who came down with leprosy were sent to the far end of the island of Molokai. Here they had to remain as long as they lived.

The lepers had little to live for. Since people feared to help them, the leper colony on Molokai once was a sorry place. The lepers lived in caves or badly built homes that were not even fit for beasts. Their food was bad. And because they were not allowed to leave their colony, they often did not have the simple tools and goods they needed.

One day, many years ago, a kind-hearted man named Father Damien heard of the uncomfortable life the lepers led on Molokai. He set off across the ocean to try to help them. After a long trip he landed on the island of Hawaii. Then he made his way to the leper colony on the island of Molokai.

When Father Damien first arrived on Molokai it was hard to imagine anything worse than the lives of the poor creatures. They crept about in search of food. There was no one to care for them. They had no doctors, no meat or bread. They had only such fruit as the coconuts and other wild things that grew in the jungles. In the whole colony there was not even one candle to give light in the dark caves where the lepers slept at night.

The good Father immediately set to work. His first job was that of helping the lepers to clean up the colony. It was not easy to make a start. The men, women, and children did not think they had much to live for. They were not interested even when they knew they might be in the colony for many years.

But Father Damien's courage soon began to change things. The people learned to love him. Within a month or two they were beginning to work to make better homes.

Best of all, Father Damien wrote to tell the story of the lepers on Molokai. He asked people in all parts of the world to send gifts and money to the distant island. The hearts of people everywhere were touched by the good man's courage in living with the lepers without fear. Many who heard of his works were moved to send food, tools, clothes, and such things. They wanted to help to make the leper colony a fine and comfortable place.

Soon there was no longer reason to be ashamed of the way the lepers had been sent off to Molokai. Schools were built for the children. Doctors came to help the sick. And steps were taken to find ways of treating leprosy so that lepers could live happier and more comfortable lives.

Through Father Damien's good works hundreds of gifts found their way to the colony on Molokai during the many years he lived there. Yet the greatest gift of all was given to them by the good man. One Sunday he met the lepers in the church they had built soon after he had come to the Hawaiian Islands.

For as long as any leper could remember, Father Damien always had spoken to them in church as "my children" or as "dear friends." Now for the first time he said, "We lepers." After his long years in the colony, the good man, too, was a leper. Father Damien's great gift was the gift of himself.

Today the struggle against leprosy as a dangerous sickness has almost been won. Few men did more to help than did good Father Damien.

Thoughts That Make Men Great

"No man has a right to do as he pleases, except when he pleases to do right."

C. Simmons

"Every brave man is a man of his word."

Corneille

"By the streets of 'by and by,' one arrives at the house of 'never.' "

Cervantes

"When you make a mistake, don't look back at it long. Take the reason of the thing into your mind, and then look forward. Mistakes are lessons of wisdom."

H. White

"If you wish to please people, you must begin by understanding them."

Charles Reade

"Do little things now; so shall big things come to you by and by asking to be done."

Persian Proverb

"Every great work is at first impossible."

Carlyle

Storybook Gardens

On the islands of the Pacific, children live happily. One of their favorite pastimes is making tiny gardens to tell stories.

For a storybook garden, choose a part of a tale you like best. It might be a part from Heidi. You might show Heidi on the mountain as she saves the young goat.

To make a garden, you will need a pan. For mountains you may use rocks. Trees and bushes can be small plants. Fences can be made from toothpicks, or by planting a row of pea or bean seeds. Water can be a piece of glass, and a road, white sand.

Plant grass seed or moss for fields. For people and animals use pipe cleaners, or make them of clay.

When everything is ready, cover the bottom of the pan with tiny stones. Fill it almost full with good ground. Put all your plants in place. Push the ground tightly around them. Put a few drops of water on the ground. Now make hills, roads, and mountains. Put in tiny animals, people, and houses. Keep tall things back of shorter ones.

To care for your garden, water it a little every day. In a short time the plants will grow. You will soon have a real storybook garden. When people come to see your garden, tell them the story of your living picture.

The Talking Tree

Far off, and in days of old when fairies lived in the woods and giants lived in the hills, there was a young soldier. After a time he grew tired of fighting the king's wars and asked to go home.

The soldier, who was called Otto, received from the king the money he had earned. He set out for the farm on which he had grown up. The king had given him two pieces of silver and a fine golden chain to put around his neck. Otto felt rich, indeed, when he left the city near which the army had camped.

He walked along under the hot summer sun on the dirt road that led him through a small woods. Soon Otto met an old woman. She was a sorry sight, with white hair and work-worn hands. Only her eyes, her clear blue eyes, did not seem aged and tired.

The old woman stopped Otto on the road. "Please, young sir," she asked, "will you give me something? I am hungry and need to buy a bit of bread to eat."

Otto was a very kind-hearted fellow. He gave the aged woman one of his two pieces of silver. Then he went swinging down the wooded trail.

A short while later the soldier came to a small stream. He crossed this little river by walking over a fallen tree trunk. There he sat down on a stump to eat his noonday meal of cold meat and dark brown bread. As he finished the last of his sandwich an old man came along. He was very old, indeed, and walked with the help of a stick.

"Good soldier," said the old fellow, "I have walked far this day and am very hungry. Do you have any food that you could give me?"

"I'm sorry," Otto told him, "but I've just eaten the last of the little that I had. However, I passed an inn down the road. You can get something to eat from the innkeeper."

The old man appeared about to weep. His old hands shook on the stick he carried. He stood still before Otto without speaking. After a minute the soldier said, "Could it be that you have nothing with which to pay for a meal at the inn? Here old fellow, take my last piece of silver. I know what it means to be hungry."

Otto gave the old man his second silver piece. Then he quickly set off on his way. The poor man's thanks were still ringing loudly in his ears.

Along toward sundown, Otto found himself wandering beside a high fence. It ran along the well-kept hayfields near a large castle. As he was beginning to think of where he might spend the night he heard someone crying.

Then, in the gathering darkness, the soldier saw a small boy. He was seated with his back to the fence. Big tears streamed from the child's eyes and his small shoulders shook with weeping. As he drew nearer, Otto saw that the boy was hardly more than a child. He was a page from the castle nearby.

Otto spoke to him kindly. "Come, my boy," he said, "things can't be as bad as all that. Tell me your troubles and perhaps I can help you."

In a little while the boy got himself in hand. Then he spilled out his sad tale. "Oh, sir," he said, "the great ruler of the castle, the rich duke whose page and servant I am, sent me to town this morning. He gave me one of his swords. He told me to have it sharpened to a fine cutting edge.

"I did as he ordered. Then on the way home . . . On the way . . . . On the . . . ." The page's story stopped for a moment as he again burst into tears. He could not go on with his tale.

Otto cheered the little page as best he could. At last the boy could continue his story. "On my way back to the castle some men jumped from the shadows in the dark woods. After taking the duke's sword from me, they ran off with it.

"Oh, believe me," the page finished his story, "I struggled to keep the sword. But they struck me down and I could not stop them from stealing it."

"Well," said Otto as cheerfully as he could, "why don't you just tell the rich duke what happened. He will chase the men. After they are caught he will have his fine sword back again."

"But you don't know the duke," the boy explained. "He will have me whipped within an inch of my life. He will beat me like a drum, and I will be lucky if he doesn't break my bones. He will whip me first. Then he will chase after the men who have his sword."

Otto thought for a moment. "See here," he said at last. "Perhaps I can still help you.

"Around my neck," Otto continued, "I have a golden chain. It is an excellent chain; a prize of war. I was in the king's army for five years to earn it.

"With a gold chain like this one, a man could buy two or perhaps three swords like the one you lost for your master, the duke." As he spoke, Otto took the heavy chain from around his neck. He placed it in the page's trembling hands.

"Take my chain to the duke. Tell him that a foolish stranger gave it to you for the sword. It is a good trade—a prize that will please the duke. I am certain that he will not whip or beat you when you give him so great a gift in place of the sword."

No sooner had Otto finished speaking than a surprising thing happened. The young page stepped backward. He began to change in looks. In less time than it takes words to tell, the boy became a fairylike creature of unbelievable beauty—a creature that shone with unearthly light.

The fairy creature spoke to Otto in a way that made him think of distant bells ringing in a church. The fairy voice sounded like bells in an old cathedral on a cold star-filled winter's night. "What a good man you are, Otto," the fairy said. "When I came to you as a poor old woman, and again as a tired old man, you gave me your last two silver pieces. And now you would give the golden chain you worked so hard to earn to a foolish boy who had lost his master's sword.

"It pleases me, Otto, to give you back your chain. And I will give you any three wishes that you believe will make you happy."

"That isn't easy," Otto said after he had overcome his great surprise. "I have my good arms and legs. I am well and happy—so for what can I ask. All I want is a long life and a good one!"

"You shall have it," said the fairy creature. "And when you return to the farm where you were born, I shall once again help you by making you rich. But you will never know that I shall help you. Rather, you will sleep now. When you open your eyes in the morning you will not remember me."

As the fairy spoke, Otto's eyes fell shut. He slid slowly to the earth in a deep sleep.

The sun shone on Otto's face the next morning and made him open his eyes. He got to his feet quickly. He felt for his gold chain and his sword to make sure that they were still with him.

"How silly of me to fall asleep here in the open fields," he told himself. "I might have had my throat cut by someone who planned to steal my golden chain." Then he set out for the nearest inn to buy breakfast.

The fairy, having no use for it, had returned his silver.

In two days of fast walking Otto reached the small farm town. Here he had lived with his grandmother and grandfather before he had run away to be a soldier in the army of the king.

His old grandmother wept with joy. She was so happy to see the huge young man into whom her grandson had grown in five years. But the homecoming was sad, too. Otto learned that his grandfather was no longer alive.

"And I have other very bad news I must tell you," the grandmother continued. "Your dear grandfather, before he died, gave a hundred pieces of gold to our neighbor, Rudi. It was all the money we had saved in a lifetime of hard work. We wanted Rudi to keep the money safe for us in his iron strongbox.

"We thought that Rudi was our friend. But now he says that your grandfather never gave him the gold. All we now have is the little that I can scratch from the earth of our farm. We cannot prove that Rudi has the gold. No one saw your grandfather take the gold from its hiding place in the woods and give it to the man."

"Never you mind, little grandmother," Otto told her. "Tomorrow I shall see the mayor of our town. We will find a way to make this Rudi bring forth the gold he has taken from us. Somehow I feel that good luck is with us. Why I feel this way I cannot tell you."

Early the next morning Otto went off to see the mayor. He wanted to learn what could be done to prove that Rudi had his grandfather's gold. The mayor called together the men and women of the town. He asked them to come to the marketplace to hear what Otto had to say. He told them that Otto had newly arrived home from the wars. Rudi, too, was ordered to come to the square.

Otto told the story, just as he had heard it from his grandmother. "After I left to fight for our king," he began, "my grandfather began to worry. He was afraid that someone might find the gold he had saved during a long lifetime of hard work. He feared that someone would steal it from its hiding place in an old hollow oak tree that stands deep in the Old Woods.

"Grandfather thought that Rudi, the rich merchant, was his friend. He took Rudi with him to the oak tree. There he gave him the heavy bag with a hundred gold pieces in it. Rudi promised to keep the gold in his iron strongbox until my grandmother had need of it or till I came home from the wars."

Rudi, a tall, fat fellow with a sharp eye, laughed aloud when Otto had told his story. "A likely tale!" he cried. "It is a fairy story that not even a child would believe. Do you, my neighbors, think that I would steal from a friend?"

The crowd was quiet as Rudi spoke. It was true that no one liked him overmuch. But anyone

would have had to admit that Otto certainly had not proved that his grandfather had given the family gold to Rudi.

At last the mayor spoke kindly words to Otto. "My boy," he began, "who saw your grandfather give the hundred gold pieces to Rudi as you say he did?"

"There was no one to see him do so," Otto had to admit. "They were alone at the tall oak tree in the Old Woods."

"Then I could hardly have the gold pieces in my strongbox!" Rudi cried loudly. "I have never been in the Old Woods. I have never even seen your grandfather's gold."

Otto found himself in a bad spot. He did not know what to do. Yet he was certain that fat Rudi had his money. Then the queerest thing happened! Otto began to hear a clear, small voice in his ear. It seemed that he had heard that voice before. But for the life of him he could not remember where.

It was, to be sure, the good fairy who had promised to help Otto. The creature had made itself very small. By magic it had hidden itself from the eyes of everyone in the crowd.

To his surprise, Otto heard HIS voice saying words that the fairy put in his mouth! The voice was his own, but the words were the fairy's!

"Hold on!" Otto heard himself say. "Hold on there, Master Rudi. The oak tree was one thing that saw my grandfather give you the gold. The old tree also heard your promise to keep the money safely hidden in your strongbox for grandmother and me.

"Let us send someone bearing the mayor's gold chain-of-office to order the tree to come to the marketplace. It can tell us what it heard."

All the people in the town square laughed long and loud at Otto's words. How stupid he was to think that a great oak tree would march to town just because it was told to do so. Even poor Otto thought that his words sounded silly, but he could not help himself.

Rudi laughed the longest and the loudest of anyone. At last he said, "Dear mayor, let us do as Master Otto asks. Give your gold chain-of-office to one of the townsmen. Send him to this old oak—if there is such a tree. Have him hold up the chain in front of the tree and order it to come here to the town square. If the old oak can prove Otto's wild tale, then gladly will I give a hundred pieces of gold to Otto and the old woman."

Again the crowd rocked and shook with laughter. This was becoming funny, indeed.

"Very well," said the good and just mayor of the town. "I will send a soldier to the tree with my golden chain. He will hold the chain high. In a loud voice he will order the tree to prove that Otto's grandfather really gave his gold to Master Rudi. But if the tree cannot prove that Otto's tale is true let us hear no more of this wild story of stolen gold."

The mayor took the heavy gold chain-of-office from about his neck. He gave it to one of the town soldiers. "Carry this to the Old Woods and find the hollow oak," he told the man. "Hold the chain high. Order the tree to prove that Otto's grandfather turned his gold over to Master Rudi for safekeeping. Then we will see what happens and settle this stupid fight over the money for once and for all."

The soldier went on his way down the path to the woods. The townspeople settled down to see what would happen. In a short while Otto once again heard the fairy voice in his ear. Once more he found strange words coming from his mouth.

"Master Mayor and Master Rudi," he found himself saying, "have we time to go to the inn for a bit of breakfast? I will be pleased to buy some milk and some sweet-cakes for us if there be time enough to eat them."

Fat Rudi, delighted at the idea of some free food, at once spoke up in a voice that many heard. "I will be glad to have some breakfast," he began. "The soldier has not yet had time to reach the tree, since it is an hour's walk."

The mayor and Rudi went with Otto to the inn. There they sat outside in the yard eating and drinking in the morning sunlight.

After many minutes had passed, Otto once more heard his voice. It was saying, "Do you think, Master Rudi, that the soldier has yet reached the oak tree? Perhaps we should go back to the marketplace and wait for the soldier to return. Or would you like to eat another cake?" Rudi had his eye on the sweet-cakes that Otto was buying. He replied, "The soldier has reached the tree by now. But it will take him another hour to march back. Do pass me another of those delicious cakes, and more milk, too, if you please." Both the mayor and the innkeeper heard Master Rudi's answer to Otto's question.

Late in the morning, in fact it was nearly noon, the mayor, Otto, and Rudi returned to the marketplace. The little town square was still crowded with people waiting to see what would happen. They looked at Otto, Rudi, and the mayor.

Just at noon, as the bell in the old church tower was striking, the soldier returned. He was bearing the mayor's golden chain in his hand. He was hot and tired after his long, fast walk under the summer sun. When the fellow had caught his breath, the mayor took the chain-of-office and put it around his neck. Then he spoke up so that all could hear.

"Tell us, good soldier," he asked, "did you find the hollow oak tree that stands deep in the Old Woods?"

"That I did," said the man.

"And did you order the tree to prove that Otto's grandfather gave Master Rudi the bag of gold?"

"That I did, Sir Mayor," the soldier replied. "I held your golden chain high. In the name of the mayor I called upon the oak tree to come here to the marketplace to prove that Rudi had taken Otto's money."

"Now answer me carefully, fellow," the mayor said. "Did the tree do anything to prove the truth of Otto's tale? Did it speak? Did it move?"

It was very quiet in the square as every ear was turned to hear the soldier's reply.

"Nothing happened," the soldier said. "There was only the sound of the warm summer wind moving through the great oak tree's leaves and branches. There was nothing to prove Otto's story."

Again, suddenly, Otto found himself speaking loudly and clearly in a voice that was not his own. "But Master Mayor," he cried, "the old oak HAS proved my story to be true, even as I had hoped!" All eyes in the marketplace were fastened on Otto as he went on.

"Rudi said that he had never been deep in the Old Woods. He said that there might not even be an old, hollow oak. Yet when I invited him to breakfast, he said that there was plenty of time to eat. He knew exactly when the soldier would reach the tree. You, Master Mayor, and the innkeeper, too, heard Rudi himself say, 'The soldier has reached the tree by now, but it will take him another hour to march back.' The tree HAS proved that fat Rudi was there. Else how would he know when the soldier would return! The oak truly was a talking tree, only Rudi spoke for it!"

All eyes now turned on Rudi, who became very red in the face. Since he was really quite stupid he knew not what to say when he found himself caught by his own words. "I . . . I . . . . I . . . . ." was all that came forth when he tried to find something to say.

"So!" the good mayor said in a voice that struck out like a whip. "You, Rudi, DID take the gold. Now then hear me. You must give Otto the one hundred

gold pieces from your iron strongbox and ten more pieces of gold for the interest on his money. Also, I fine you fifty gold pieces for trying to steal the money."

Poor fat Rudi could only tremble and say nothing when he heard what the mayor ordered. As for the townspeople, they cheered Otto. They cheered him for his good luck, for his riches, and for being so wise as to catch Master Rudi in his wrongdoing. They carried Otto around the square on their shoulders. Then they danced all afternoon to show their delight at seeing Rudi's bad ways trip him up at last.

As for Otto, he at first felt queer indeed because of the way he had found himself speaking words that someone else seemed to say for him at just the right time. Of course, he never knew that it was really the fairy creature who had got back his gold for him. In time he got used to the idea that he himself had been sharp enough to beat Rudi at Rudi's own game.

As the good fairy had promised, Otto had a long and happy life. He married the mayor's beautiful daughter. Some years later he became the mayor of his little town. He was always kind and good, so the fairy never had reason to be sorry that he had helped the one-time soldier on the path to happiness.

Think Twice

Otto was a just and wise mayor. He always knew how to help his people. One time a rich man gave his farm to the town.

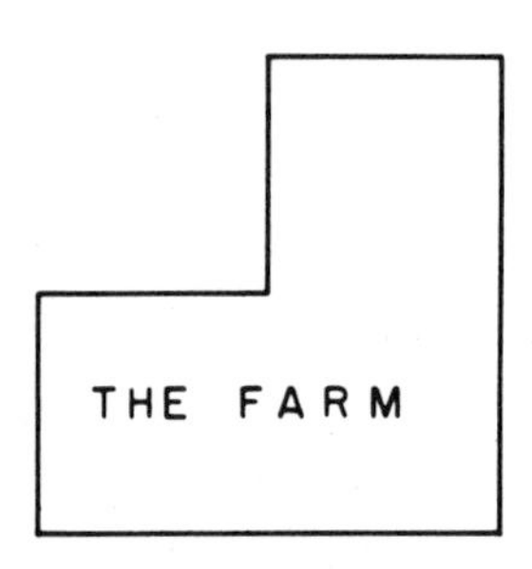

The rich man told the people they could use it for whatever they pleased. But they could not agree on what they wanted.

One group said, "We want a park." "No," said a second group, "we want a place for the children to play." A third group said, "We want a church." "Oh, no!" said a fourth group. "We want a place for a school."

Then the fairy whispered into the mayor's ear. Otto found himself saying, "Very well, each of you shall have a part of the land. I will cut it into four parts. Each part will be exactly *the same size* and *the same shape* as the others." How did he do it? Look at the picture. Try it. Then look on page 237.

. . . . .

One day the fairy showed Otto a trick with numbers. He told the mayor how to multiply any number by 9 without multiplying at all.

The fairy said, "Write down the number you want to multiply. Put a 0 after the number. Then write the same number below it without the 0. Now subtract."

Otto choose the number 976. He wrote 9760. Below it he wrote $\underline{976}$ and subtracted to get 8784.

Try it with any number. Do you know the fairy's trick? If not, look on page 237.

BRAVE DEEDS

Oh, it is excellent to have
a giant's strength.

Shakespeare

A knight there was, and that a worthy man,
That from the time that he first began
To riden out . . .

— *Chaucer*

A knight must prove always
to be true.
to be brave.
to be kind.
to love his land.
to be a gentleman.
to fight for what is
just and right.
to do no wrong of which
he must be ashamed.

The Knights of the Silver Shield

There was once a great castle in a deep woods. The castle had thick walls, a high gate, and towers that were bigger than the tallest trees. The old woods that spread all around the castle was dark and dangerous, and many fierce giants lived in it.

In the castle was a group of knights who were kept there by the king of the country. It was their job to help travelers who might be in the woods and to make war on the giants whenever they could.

Each of the knights in the castle carried a magic shield. These shields were not like those of other knights, but had been made by a great magician who had lived in the castle many years before. The shields were made of silver and, when a knight was brave and good, his shield shone beautifully in the sun.

When a knight first was given his shield, it was dark and plain in color. Then, as he showed himself to be brave and kind, the shield began to sparkle until he could see his face in it as if the shield were a mirror. However, if a knight were lazy or afraid, the shield grew so dark that he became ashamed to carry it.

But this was not all. When any knight was a very fine man and did something very brave, a golden star appeared in the middle of his shield. This was the greatest thing that could happen to any man. At the time this story begins, only the captain of the castle had a gold star on his shield. The stars were very difficult, indeed, to win.

Now there came a time when the worst of the giants gathered in the woods to make war on the knights. They made a camp not far away and killed anyone who traveled along the road.

The captain told his men that on the next day he would lead

them against the giants. When they heard the news, the knights were very pleased. Here, perhaps, was a chance for them to earn a gold star for their shields.

Among the men in the castle was a new knight named Sir Roland. He was a fine soldier, and already his silver shield showed that he was brave and strong. Sir Roland was looking forward to meeting the ugly giants. He promised himself that he would do his best to chase them far away.

The next morning the captain of the knights came to Sir Roland and said, "One good man must stay here and keep watch on the gate to our castle. I have decided that you are the one who must remain behind."

Roland was sorry, very sorry, to hear the captain's order, but he said nothing. Soon the knights rode away on their horses and he was left alone.

An hour went by, then two hours, and nothing happened at the castle. A deer came out of the woods to eat grass in the shadow of the castle wall. But Roland saw no other living creature.

Then, at last, the knight at the gate saw a man coming along the road through the trees. Roland saw that it was one of his fellow knights from the castle. The man had been hit in the hand by an arrow. He was not a brave man, and the look in his eyes showed that he was frightened. "Let me watch the gate for you, Sir Roland," he cried.

Roland's heart jumped with joy. Then he remembered the captain's orders. Sadly he said, "My place is at the gate. Your place is with our knights. Go back to them."

The knight was ashamed when Sir Roland spoke. Slowly he walked back to the woods and disappeared among the trees.

After a time an old woman came along the road to the castle. She came up to Sir Roland and asked for food. He told her that no one could come into the castle that day. Then he sent a servant to bring her bread and cheese.

While she was waiting, Sir Roland asked her if she had seen the knights and the giants. "I have seen them," she said, "and things go badly for your friends. If you were a real man you would go and give them help."

Sir Roland felt so badly that he shut the gate after the old woman had her food. He did not want to listen to her any longer.

After a while the knight heard a knock at the gate. "What do you want?" he asked.

"Open the gate, Sir Roland," someone replied. The knight opened the gate and saw an old man standing a few feet away. The old fellow wore a long black coat and carried a very beautiful sword.

"You should not be here," the man said, "when your friends are having such a hard struggle with the giants."

"I have my orders," said Roland. "I must not leave this gate."

"Look here! Listen to me," the old man cried. "I have brought you this magic sword. Nothing can stand before it. Take it, my friend, and help your fellow knights to beat the giants."

Roland believed that the sword was really a magic one. He reached out his hand as though he would take it. The old man came forward as if he were going to cross over to the castle.

But again it came to Sir Roland's mind that he had been told to stay at the gate. He called out to the man, "No! Stay where you are."

The man stopped, but he waved the sword in the air and cried, "This is your last chance, Sir Knight! If you do not take it your friends will all be killed by the giants while you hide behind the castle wall!"

Roland feared that if he listened any longer, he could not make himself stay in the castle. "Close the gate," he told the servants. "I must follow my captain's orders and remain here."

As the knight said these words a strange and surprising change came over the old man. He began to grow bigger and bigger. Soon he was as tall as any giant in the great dark woods. At first Roland could not believe his eyes. Then he realized that the old fellow was really one of the giants. By magic he had made himself look like a little old man!

The knight trembled to think of what would have happened if he had taken the sword and left the gate! While Sir Roland watched, the giant angrily went off down the road and was lost to sight among the trees.

Soon after the giant had left, Sir Roland heard the sound of horses and men coming. It was the captain and his men returning to the castle. Roland signaled the servants to open the big gate and then he ran out to meet his friends.

The knights were tired and dusty, but they were full of joy because they had soundly beaten the giants. When they had all come into the castle, Sir Roland closed the gate once more. Then he hurried to follow them to the great hall.

As Roland came into the hall he found every man's eye upon him. "The shield! Look at Sir Roland's shield!" they cried.

The knight slowly looked down at the silver shield he carried. There, flaming in the middle of the shield, was a star of gold!

When Sir Roland had finished his tale, the captain spoke. "Men may make mistakes," he said, "but our magic silver shields are never wrong! You, Sir Knight, have been the greatest among us today because you would not leave the gate on which I had ordered you to keep watch. No matter how much you wanted to be with us, you stayed at your job!"

"Tell us, Sir Knight, what happened here at the castle today?" the captain asked as soon as he had gotten over his surprise. "Did the giants try to break down the gate? Did you drive them away alone?"

"No, Sir," said Roland. "Only one giant came here, and he went away quietly when he found that he could not enter the castle." Then he told of all that had happened through the long day.

Then the knights jumped to their feet and cheered Sir Roland until the great hall rang with their cries. "Long live the new knight of the golden star!"

Grace Darling

In the wild, cold ocean to the north of England and west of Norway is a small group of islands. A hundred years ago an old man named Mr. Darling was the lighthouse keeper on one of the islands. He had a daughter named Grace.

Mr. Darling and Grace lived a lonely life, but a happy one. Each night when it grew dark they turned on the huge light in the lighthouse tower so that ship captains would use it and steer clear of the sharp rocks a mile off the shore of the little island.

One dark night Grace lay in bed listening to the wild wind blow and to the cold rain drumming on her small window. As she was about to fall asleep she heard the faint sound of a ship's gun.

Ships fired off their guns when they were in trouble. Quickly Grace ran to her window and stared into the black, rain-washed night. Her heart beat faster at what she saw in the light from the lighthouse tower.

A small ship had crashed into the rocks about a mile from the shore. Great sheets of water poured over the ship when the waves struck her side.

Grace called her old father. Then the two of them threw on warm clothes and ran to the beach to see what could be done to get help to the ship.

People from the little fishing town nearby had also heard the ship fire its gun for help. In a few minutes there were forty or fifty men and women along the shore watching the ship breaking to pieces on the knife-edged rocks. They could see five men holding on for dear life as the great waves rolled over them.

Grace turned to the fishermen from the little town. "We must save those poor men!" she cried. "We can take the boat from our lighthouse."

But the fishermen were wise to the ways of the ocean. "It is useless to try to reach the men. It is far too dangerous," they told her.

"We cannot just stand here and see the men killed," Grace replied. "We must at least try to help them."

Mr. Darling could not say "No" to his brave daughter. While the fishermen stood looking on, the old fellow helped her pull the heavy lighthouse boat to the water's edge. In a few minutes they were ready and pushed away from the small sandy beach.

It was very hard to row the boat with the waves crashing about them. But Grace and her father did not give up. With the strong wind to slow them, it seemed a very long time before they drew near the distant rocks.

Then, when they were close to the ship, their work became more dangerous than ever. Only by good luck did the two of them escape striking against the rocks.

At last Mr. Darling was close enough to climb onto the ship. As quickly as he could he helped the half-frozen men into the rowboat. At last all five of them lay cold and wet on the bottom of the boat.

Once again Grace and her father began to row through the mighty waves. Now, with the load of helpless men, the small boat rode far down in the water. The wind whipped Grace's hair about her face and the cold rain made her tremble as she pulled for the far-off shore. The girl was so tired that she almost gave up hope of reaching land.

Suddenly the long, frightful trip back from the reef was ended. A wave carried the rowboat far up on the narrow sand beach. Many willing hands helped the girl, her father, and the five men to safety.

The poor men were carried to the warm kitchen in the lighthouse. There, tired as she was, Grace would have helped the other women make hot coffee and warm food if they had not put the girl to bed.

So it was that a brave girl and a fine old man saved five men from being killed by the cold waters and sharp rocks on a dark night long, long ago. Their bravery should never be forgotten.

A Riddle for a Life

Long ago there lived a king in old Greece. He had a newborn son. A wise man warned the king not to let the child grow up. "If you do," he told the king, "your son will take away your kingdom. He will be king."

Thereupon the king gave his son to a shepherd. He took the beautiful child home to his wife. As years went by, the boy grew into a brave young man.

Now in the forest nearby, there lived a huge creature. It had the body of a lion and the upper part of a woman. It lay near the roadway on top of a rock, ready to spring. As each traveler came through the forest, the creature would stop him and ask a riddle. If he could answer it, the traveler would be allowed to continue on his journey. If he could not answer it, he was killed. No one had ever been able to guess the answer.

One day the brave young man fell into the hands of the creature. He was not afraid when the lion-woman asked him this riddle:

"What animal is it which in the morning goes on four feet, at noon on two, and in the evening upon three?"

"Man," cried out the brave traveler.

The lion-woman was very angry because he guessed the riddle. With a great crash the creature threw itself from the rocks. Never again was it seen.

The people of the land were overjoyed. "Let us make this brave young man our king!" they cried. A great feast was held and the beautiful queen was given to him for a wife.

. . . . .

Can you give the answer to the riddle? If not, look on page 237.

The Brave Three Hundred

Some twenty-five hundred years ago the people of Greece found themselves at war with the army of King Xerxes. This fierce king was the ruler of many lands. He was said to have more soldiers than there were stars in the sky or sands on the ocean beach.

When Xerxes led his huge army into Greece the people gathered together their worldly goods, their families, and cattle. They hurried to hide in the wooded hills. No one was safe from the knives and arrows of Xerxes' fierce men-at-arms. And the Greeks knew it.

The kings of the small city-states and hill towns made ready to meet the soldiers of King Xerxes. But they needed time to get ready for the struggle to save their home lands. They feared that Xerxes might get through the high mountains and reach the inland plains. If he did that before their small armies could get together there was but little chance for them to save their homes.

Of all the small Greek armies, the army of Sparta led by King Leonidas made ready most quickly. Led by their brave ruler, the small band of Spartans reached the narrow mountain pass at Thermopylae. They got there before the soldiers of King Xerxes. All together there were three hundred Spartan men. One or two hundred other Greeks also had come to help hold the pass at Thermopylae. Each of the Spartans had given his promise to hold the pass as long as there was life in his body.

Like a great river the armies of Xerxes streamed toward the mountain. There were perhaps one hundred thousand of these men moving to face the small band of Greeks. The brave Spartans were standing behind their leader, King Leonidas, at the lonely pass in the bare mountain.

Each day the Greeks received word that more homes were burned and people and cattle killed at King Xerxes' orders. Each day they waited with anger growing ever greater in their hearts.

Soon the men in Xerxes' army reached Thermopylae. They made camp near the pass. The first night, as they camped on the plain, their cooking fires were many. There seemed more fires than there were stars in the blue-black sky. But the brave Spartans, if they were afraid, gave no sign of fear. Not a man trembled, and they slept quietly with their swords near at hand.

When the sun came up the next morning King Leonidas spoke bravely to his three hundred Spartans and to the small group of Greeks from other cities who were with them. "Today the men of Xerxes will try to come through the mountain pass," he began. "Let no man be afraid. The sky may be black with arrows. Be not ashamed if you feel fear in your hearts. But stand tall and straight as the arrows streak past. Stand with sword in hand. Let us see who are the better men—the dogs in the army of Xerxes or the soldiers of our homeland."

No sooner had Leonidas finished speaking than the soldiers of King Xerxes began streaming up the narrow road to the pass. Wildly they struggled under the dangerous arrows that darted above their heads. But only a few at a time could come up the pass. And these were cut to pieces by the red, swinging swords of the Spartans.

All day the soldiers, by the thousands, pushed forward. All day the Greeks struck back. They seemed to stand like a wall of iron. When one man fell, another jumped into his place.

The second day, too, the Spartans kept Xerxes' soldiers from entering the pass at Thermopylae. No Greek tried to escape. Each man seemed to enjoy the chance to lift his sword for his family and for Greece.

The mouth of the pass was a frightful place that day. Yet the brave men cheered one another and again checked the thousands of soldiers who tried to break through the mountain pass. Again, as night fell, Leonidas and his brave Spartans had won the day.

The third day of the great struggle for the road through the mountains began quietly. This time Xerxes did not at first send his men against the small Greek army at sunup. Instead King Xerxes seemed to be watching for some kind of signal.

At first Leonidas was very pleased to see that no soldiers were pouring up the road. Perhaps they had had enough! But no. Soon Leonidas saw that Xerxes' soldiers had found a small foot-trail that led them around the pass. In a moment Leonidas saw that he and his few men soon would have many soldiers coming at them from above the pass and from behind.

Leonidas saw that there would soon be soldiers on every side of him. He told all his men, save those Spartans who had promised to hold the pass, to leave. "We Spartans will do what can be done," he cried. "The others must leave now and finish this war with the help of the other Greek kings. Even now they gather to check the armies of Xerxes and send him running home."

So, by afternoon on the third day, Leonidas and his fellow Spartans—those of the three hundred who were left—made ready for their last stand. Already they had held up Xerxes for two days. Perhaps they could slow his armies a day or two more.

A rain of arrows warned the Greeks that the time had come for their last great struggle. They drew their swords and made ready for whatever might come.

Like a great wave, the soldiers of Xerxes drove into the brave men of Sparta from every side.

Now there was no one to take the place of a Greek who fell. Now there was no time to step back and let another Spartan hold one's place in the narrow pass. The fierce soldiers of Xerxes' army were on every hand. There was only one way in which the uneven struggle could end.

Brave Leonidas fell early in the afternoon, an arrow through his throat. His men carried on without a leader. They fought with their swords until these were broken. And then they went on fighting with their hands and teeth until every Greek had been beaten to the earth.

When the great fight on the third day at Thermopylae was ended, it was because only Xerxes' men lived in the pass. All of the Spartans lay where they had fallen. Their broken swords were in their quiet hands.

The great fight the brave Spartans had made against so many thousands had saved Greece. The three days that were earned so dearly gave the other Greek kings the time they needed to gather together their armies and ships.

Xerxes was in Greece only a short time when two hundred of his ships were broken to pieces in a wild sea fight. The great King of Kings had been beaten by the little Greek city-states. He had to turn back to his kingdom without becoming a ruler in the new lands.

In later years, because of the way in which Leonidas and his brave three hundred had fought, the Greeks wrote the following words on the mountain pass at Thermopylae:

Go tell the Spartans,
You who pass by,
That here to save our land,
Three hundred of us lie.

Greek Word Travelers

Magic! And all the words in the world are gone! How would you get along if there were no words to use? Try it for a few minutes. Remember there are no words to say and no words to use for thinking.

What would you do when you met someone—point, make a strange sound? Some people say that is what happened long, long ago. These strange sounds took on meaning. They became words. Some people think that in the beginning there was only one language in the world. They believe all languages came from that one language.

After a while people began to travel. They moved to new parts of the world. They took their words with them, and made up new ones. And so it came to pass that after hundreds of years, people in different parts of the world used different sounds. There came to be many languages.

Our words came from many lands. Some have had very interesting changes in meaning from the time they were first born. Let us look at some words that traveled to us from faraway Greece.

School is a funny word. Its meaning got mixed up in its travels. The Greek word meant "rest time." In days of long ago people had to work hard in the fields or in other places. The only time they had for reading or for lessons was after they had finished their day's work.

Mystery is another word traveler from Greece. There its meaning was "to shut your eyes." That is why we use it to mean something dark or hidden.

Think about words. Can you find other word travelers with interesting stories?

A Brave Deed Show

Brave deeds are fun to remember. Even more fun is to dream of an adventure you might have had. Imagine you were a knight of old. What exciting adventure did you have? Let your friends see your daring deeds in a pin-a-peek show.

Here is the way to do it.

1. Take a long piece of paper 4 inches wide. On it draw and color pictures to tell your story. See picture 1.

2. Get a shoe box. Draw and cut a line across the bottom of the box. Make it a little wider than your paper. See picture 2.

3. Do the same on the top of the box directly above the cut in the bottom. See picture 3.

4. Draw two lines across the end of the box. Make a hole to see through where the lines cross. See picture 4.

5. Make a skylight on the top of the box. Cut along the three heavy lines. Fold back on the dotted line. See picture 5.

6. Slide the end of your picture story through the cut in the lid and down through the cut in the bottom of the box. See picture 6.

Now you are ready to show your moving picture. Children of long ago used to ask their friends to pay one pin to peek at their shows.

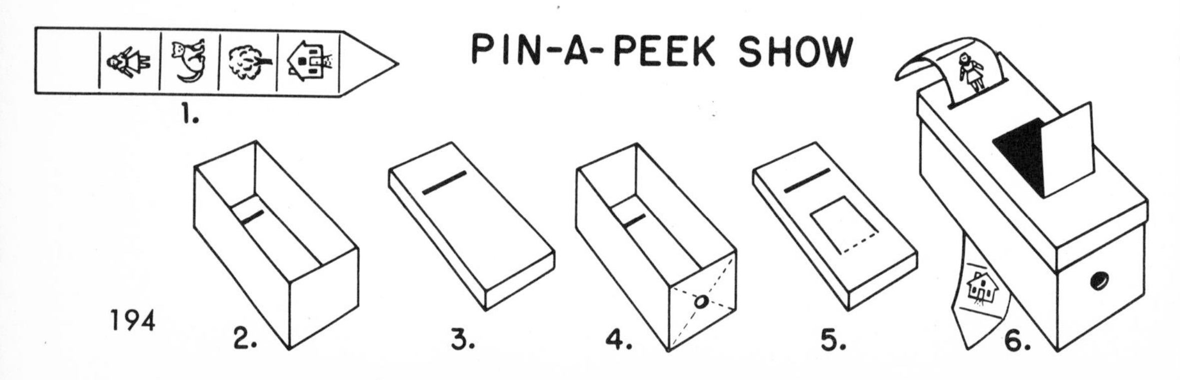

LET'S REMEMBER

The tales of old
My father told
Of merry holidays so glad and bright,
Are in my book
If you will look—
Thanksgiving, Christmas, and Halloween night.

John's Pumpkin

Last spring I found a pumpkin seed,
And thought that I would go
And plant it in a secret place,
That no one else would know,
And watch it all summer long to see
It grow and grow and grow,
And maybe raise a pumpkin for
A Jack-a-Lantern show.

I stuck a stick beside the seed,
And thought that I would shout
One morning when I stooped and saw
The greenest little sprout!
I used to carry water there,
When no one was about,
And every day I'd count to see
How many leaves were out.

Till by and by there came a flower
The color of the sun,
Which withered up, and then I saw
The pumpkin had begun;
But oh! I knew I'd have to wait
So long to have my fun,
Before that small green ball could be
A great big yellow one.

At last, one day, when it had grown
To be the proper size,
Said Aunt Matilda: "John, see here,
I'll give you a surprise!"
She took me to a pantry shelf,
And there before my eyes,
Was set *a dreadful row of half*
A dozen pumpkin pies.

Said Aunt Matilda, "John, I found
A pumpkin high and dry,
Upon a pile of rubbish, down
Behind that worn-out sty!"
O, dear, I didn't cry, because
I'm quite too big to cry,
But honestly, I couldn't eat
A mouthful of that pie.

Mrs. Archibald

The Night of the Twelve Witches

Long, long ago, in the days when the Little People were about, there lived in Ireland a rich woman. She had eight lovely children. On the night before Halloween she sat up late. She was sewing a party dress for one of her daughters. All the family were asleep. Suddenly there came a knock on the door. A voice called, "Open! open!"

"Who is there?" called the woman of the house.

"I am the Witch of One Horn," the voice replied.

The rich woman thought it was one of her neighbors who came for help. She opened the door, and a woman pushed in past her. The visitor had some cloth in her hand. In the middle of her head, right above her eyes, was a horn. It looked as if it were growing there.

The horned woman sat down by the fire very quietly. All that could be heard was the whistling of the wind around the house. Her needle flew back and forth as she sewed a strange-looking black coat.

Suddenly the witch stopped sewing and said aloud, "Where are the women? They are too long in coming."

Then a second knock was heard at the door. A voice called as before, "Open! open!"

The rich woman got up and opened the door. A second witch pushed past her. In her hand was some black thread. On her head were two horns.

"Give me a place by the fire," she cried. "I am the Witch of Two Horns." Without a sound she sat down by the fire and began sewing.

Again there was a knock at the door. More witches came in.

The room was very still. All that could be heard was a low crying of the wild wind outside, which went like this:

Strange to hear and frightening to look upon were these twelve witches.

The rich woman tried to rise from her chair to call for help but she could not move. The spell of the witches was upon her.

Then one of the witches called to her and said, "Rise, woman, and make us a cake." But the rich woman could find no water to put with the flour.

"Take this and bring water from the town well," said one. And the witch handed her a pot with a hundred holes in the bottom of it.

The rich woman took the pot and went to the well. The more water she poured into the top, the more ran through the holes. At last she sat down by the well and cried.

Then a voice told her, "Take some mud and grass. Put them together and fill the holes so that the water will stay in the pot."

She did this. Then the voice said again, "Now go home. When you come to the north corner of your house, stand outside and cry in a loud voice three times, 'The mountain of the witch women and the sky above it are on fire!' "

The rich woman did as she was told. The witches inside the house heard the call. With a terrible cry they rushed out the door. Back to the "mountain of the witch women" they flew.

Then the voice, which was really the Spirit of the Wind, spoke again. "Enter your house and prepare it against the witches, lest they return.

"First," said the Spirit, "splash some water outside your door. Then take the cake which the witches made while you were gone. Break it into little pieces. Put a little piece into the mouth of each one of your children while they sleep. Next, take the cloth on which the witches were sewing. Put it half in and half out of the box on the table. And last, fasten the door with a huge wooden board."

When the rich woman had done these things, she waited. She heard a sound outside.

"Open, open, wooden door!" cried the witches to the door.

"I cannot," said the door, "for I am fastened with a huge board. I have no power to move."

"Open, open, witches' cake!" they cried again.

"I cannot," said the cake, "for I am in the mouths of the sleeping children."

Thereupon, with a wild cry, the witches rushed through the air, back to the mountain.

The rich woman and her family were never troubled again. On the way up into the air one of the witches lost her coat. The rich woman kept it always to remember "The Night of the Twelve Witches."

Thanksgiving Day

Over the river and through the wood,
To grandfather's house we go;
The horse knows the way
To carry the sleigh
Through the white and drifted snow.

Over the river and through the wood—
Oh, how the wind does blow!
It stings the toes
And bites the nose,
As over the ground we go.

Over the river and through the wood,
To have a first-rate play;
Hear the bells ring,
"Ting-a-ling-ding!"
Hurrah for Thanksgiving Day!

Over the river and through the wood,
Trot fast, my dapple gray!
Spring over the ground,
Like a hunting hound,
For this is Thanksgiving Day.

Over the river and through the wood,
And straight through the barn-yard gate,
We seem to go
Extremely slow—
It is so hard to wait!

Over the river and through the wood—
Now Grandmother's cap I spy.
Hurrah for the fun!
Is the pudding done?
Hurrah for the pumpkin pie!

Lydia Maria Child

Fun at Grandmother's House

While the children waited for Thanksgiving dinner at Grandmother's house, all the uncles, aunts, and cousins played games. Here are two favorite games of long ago which you may like, too.

Grandmother Comes to Thanksgiving Dinner

The leader begins by saying, "Grandmother has come to our house for Thanksgiving dinner but she doesn't like peas. What can you give her instead?"

Perhaps the first player will then answer "carrots." That is correct. If the next player should say "turnips," he would be out because the letter *p* is in *turnips*.

The trick is that at first everyone thinks the vegetable *peas* is meant instead of the letter *p*. Even after the trick is discovered, the game is fun because it is very easy to make a mistake. A player must give a word without the letter *p* in it before the leader counts to five.

A Thanksgiving Hunt

The players form a ring. One is chosen to be the "hunter." He is given a nut which he is to drop in back of someone in the ring. As he walks around the outside of the ring, he sings,

"Hunt the rabbit in the woods,
I lost him, I found him.
Hunt the rabbit in the woods,
I lost him, I found him.
I won't catch you,
And I won't catch you,
But I will catch *you*."

He drops the nut as he sings the last line. The child in back of whom the nut falls must pick it up and run around the ring. He tries to get back to his place before the "hunter" gets there. If he fails, he becomes the hunter.

A Turkey for the Stuffing

It was the day before Thanksgiving. Ben turned from the window through which he had been looking at the river. "Tomorrow will be Thanksgiving Day," he said to his grandmother. "The people next door are going to have a turkey. What are we going to have?"

Grandmother looked at her grandson's thin face and at his clean but worn-out clothes. Then she said sadly, "What do you think we are going to have?"

Ben did not answer. The happy look disappeared from his face. He did not need to be told that there was only the plainest food in their little house.

After a little while Ben said, "Tell me about a real Thanksgiving dinner."

His grandmother took off her eyeglasses. There was a faraway look in her eyes. After she had sat down in the old kitchen rocking chair she said, "I know of one Thanksgiving when your father was still here when we had a dinner fit for a king. There was a ten-pound turkey and bread stuffing. Even mince pie that I made with my own hands . . ." The poor woman's words trailed off and a tear slipped down her soft old face.

"Maybe we could have some stuffing," Ben said quickly when he saw how sad his grandmother felt.

The old lady's face cleared and she smiled. "So we could!" she said. "I never would have thought of having stuffing without the turkey! We have potatoes, too, and some beans. Why, we can have a real feast, Ben!"

On Thanksgiving morning, grandmother began to make the stuffing. She put dry bread in a bowl, then an egg, and milk, and many other things. "Now, Ben," she said at last, "run down along the river bank and find some wood. We'll want a hot fire when I cook our stuffing."

Ben ran down to the water's edge. While he was picking up old bits of wood a big, long boat came slowly down the river. The captain stood at the wheel. When he saw Ben he called out, "Hello there, son! What makes you work so hard on Thanksgiving Day?"

"I'm waiting for dinner to cook," Ben called back.

"Going to have turkey, I suppose?" the captain asked.

"No, but we're going to have turkey stuffing!" Ben said proudly.

"Turkey stuffing, but no turkey!" said the captain in surprise. "Well, if that isn't the strangest dinner I ever heard of." Then he looked more closely at Ben and saw that the boy's clothes were poor and worn thin.

More kindly, the captain said, "And what else are you going to have? Mince pie without any mincemeat in it?"

"No, sir!" Ben said loudly and clearly. "My father had mince pie for Thanksgiving dinner once, though."

"He did, did he?" said the captain. Then he turned to the man near him. Quietly he said, "Did you hear that? The poor boy has nothing but stuffing for dinner today.

"Run tell the cook to cut our turkey in half," the captain ordered. "Tell him to bring it here right away, and one of our two mince pies. Yes, and you'd better bring me that box of oranges, too."

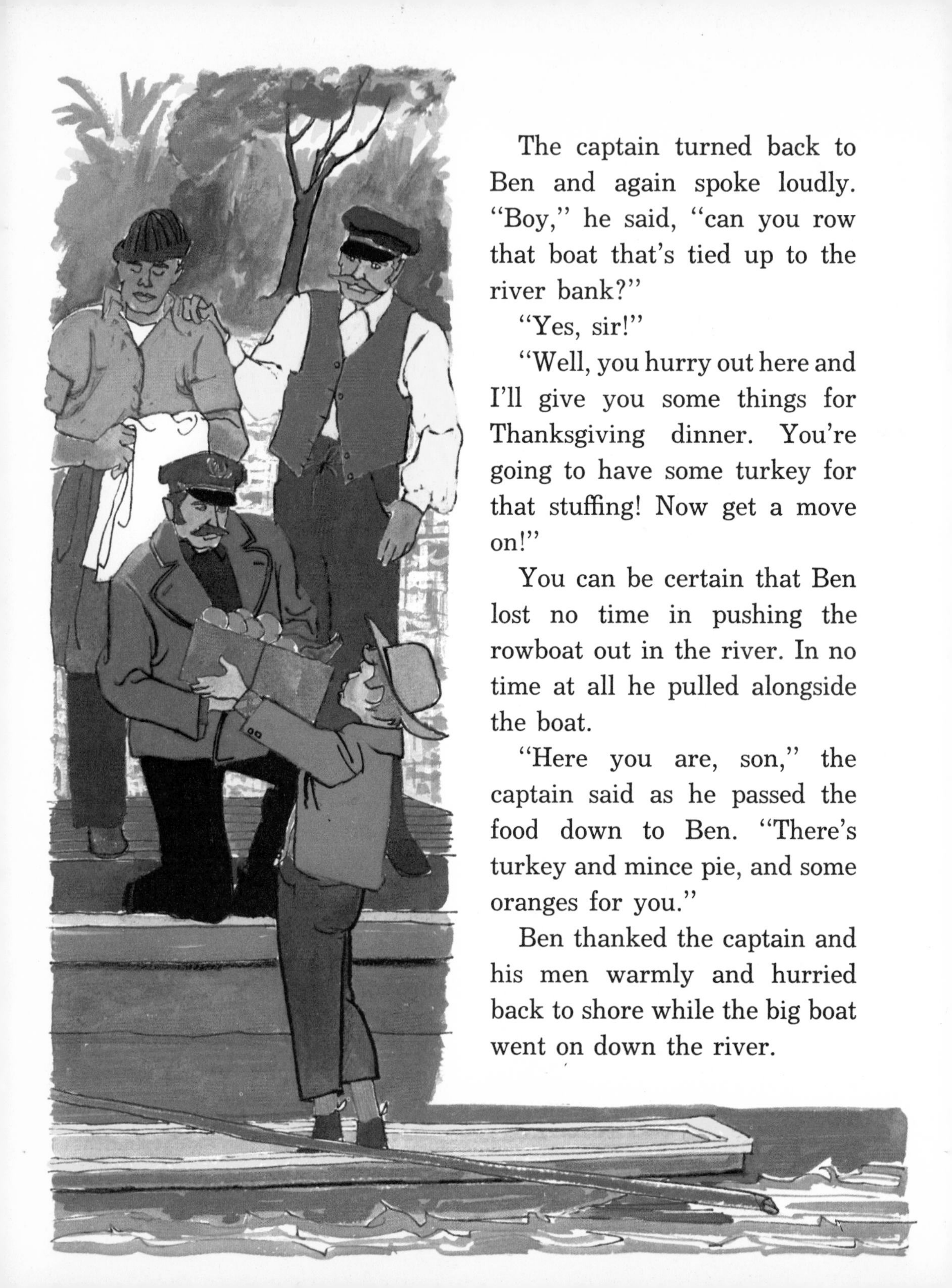

The captain turned back to Ben and again spoke loudly. "Boy," he said, "can you row that boat that's tied up to the river bank?"

"Yes, sir!"

"Well, you hurry out here and I'll give you some things for Thanksgiving dinner. You're going to have some turkey for that stuffing! Now get a move on!"

You can be certain that Ben lost no time in pushing the rowboat out in the river. In no time at all he pulled alongside the boat.

"Here you are, son," the captain said as he passed the food down to Ben. "There's turkey and mince pie, and some oranges for you."

Ben thanked the captain and his men warmly and hurried back to shore while the big boat went on down the river.

Ben ran to the house and burst into the kitchen. "Look at this, Grandmother!" he cried. "Oh, boy! Are we lucky! First, stuffing, and now turkey for the stuffing!"

Far down the river the captain and his men sat down to their Thanksgiving dinner.

"You know," said the cook, "this turkey is mighty good to eat, even if I say so myself. And do you know why, Captain? Because you gave half of it away!"

"Yes," said the captain, "I wouldn't have enjoyed a bite of our food if I'd known that boy had no turkey for the stuffing!"

A Thanksgiving Sing

In grandfather's day when Thanksgiving dinner was over, the family gathered around to sing. A favorite song of boys and girls who lived in the mountain country was *Grandma Good*.

Grandma Good

Grandma Good said a very strange thing,
"Boys may whistle but girls must sing!"
That is what I heard her say,
'Twas no longer than yesterday.
Boys can whistle (boys whistle),
Girls must sing, tra-la-la-la-la.

Boys can whistle, of course they may,
They can whistle the live long day.
Why can't girls whistle too, pray tell,
If they're able to do it well.
Boys can whistle (boys whistle),
Girls must sing, tra-la-la-la-la.

Grandma Good
Traditional
Grand-ma Good said a ver – y strange thing,
Boys can whistle, of course they may,
"Boys can whistle but girls must sing!"
They can whistle the live long day.
That is what I heard her say,
Why can't girls whistle too pray tell,
'Twas no longer than yes – ter – day.
If they're a – ble to do it well.
Boys can whistle, (whistle)
Boys can whistle, (whistle)
Girls must sing, tra – la – la – la – la.
Girls must sing, tra – la – la – la – la.

The Unhappy Little Fir Tree

Far out in the woods stood a pretty little fir tree. He was not more than two feet tall. However, the baby tree stood in a good place in the sun and fresh air where he would quickly grow tall and strong.

The woods near at hand were beautiful. Flowers grew among the trees. Children from the city came to play, and wild animals made their homes in the deep shadows. You would think that the little fir could have been the happiest tree in the world. But he wasn't!

You see, the baby fir tree thought only of growing up. He looked at his brothers who were five or ten feet high and he wanted to be like them. They seemed so huge and strong!

One day, as often happened, some children passed by. The baby fir caught a girl's eye and she called out to a friend, "How pretty this little one is!" But was the fir tree happy to be called pretty? Not at all! He was sad because the girl had said that he was little!

The next year the fir tree had grown taller, and the year after, he was taller still. "If only I were as tall as my brothers," the small tree said to himself. "Then I could look far out over the wide world. Birds would build nests in my branches, and when the wind blew, it would sing through my needles and move me from side to side. BUT I AM JUST TOO SMALL!"

So the unhappy little fir tree found no pleasure in the beautiful world about him.

The next winter, when the fir tree was four years old, some men came into the woods. It was a short while before Christmas.

The men looked carefully at many of the fir trees that were ten or eleven feet tall. Then they cut down some of the very best ones. After that the men tied down the tree branches with ropes and loaded them on big sleds. Then a team of horses pulled them away.

"Where can my brothers be going?" asked the fir tree, but there was no one to hear his question except a rabbit. And the rabbit did not know the answer.

The next day some birds flew by the unhappy little fir tree and stopped to rest in his snowy branches. "Tell me, please," he asked the birds, "where were the men taking my brothers on the big sled?"

"We know! We know!" the little birds replied. "They are going to the great city for Christmas. Your brothers will be Christmas trees. We will see them through the windows in the houses, just as we did last year."

"Go on, please go on!" said the fir tree, his needles trembling because he was so interested in the story.

"Well," the birds said, "the Christmas trees are planted in a very warm room and people dress them up with the most beautiful things! On their branches they hang fruit and candy and honey-cakes. Yes, and paper chains and toys, too. But the beautiful colored lights on the green branches are best of all!"

"Please tell me more about the lights," cried the fir tree. But the little birds flew away and never answered his question. "How I wish that I might be a Christmas tree," the little tree said to the wind. He felt more unhappy than ever because he was so small.

"Listen!" said the wind. "I, too, go to the city. I, too, have seen your brothers sparkling with a thousand beautiful many-colored lights. But you do NOT want to be a Christmas tree."

"And why not?" said the sad fir tree in surprise.

"Because soon the people take away your beautiful candy and cakes and eat them. The children take the toys from your branches. You begin to look old and broken. Then, in a week or two, the people take away all your colored lights.

They carry you into the yard, and burn you up!''

If there was anything of which the trees were most afraid, it was fire. Yet the unhappy fir tree replied bravely to the wind, "I do not care if they burn me up," he declared. "Just let me grow tall. Just let me be beautiful with the colored lights in my branches. Just let me make people happy for a short while. Then let them burn me up!"

"Have it as you wish," said the wind. "You are really a fine little tree, and next Christmas the men will take you!" and the wind blew off and disappeared.

The snow melted, the spring and summer passed, and the snow again lay white and lovely on the ground. Christmas drew near.

The men returned, and two of them stopped to look at the unhappy fir tree.

"This one is a real beauty," the taller man said. "I think he is the tree for us!"

"Yes, your children will like it," the other man replied. "Let us come back at the very end of the day to get it."

When the men walked away, the fir tree was both happy and sad. At last he would go with his brothers. He would make people happy at Christmas—yet in a week or two he would be burned, and nothing would remain of his lovely green branches.

All day long the fir tree watched the men work. He saw the trees fall and he saw them slowly fill the huge sled. At last, near sundown, the men came back to him. Now it was his turn to go.

The fir tree waited bravely to be cut and to crash to the cold, snow-covered ground. But —what was happening?

The men were not cutting his trunk. They were digging into the frozen earth. They were taking him out of the ground—roots and all! Before he knew it, the tree found himself lifted out of the ground. Then the two men carefully wrapped his roots in an old brown cloth bag. A minute later he was on top of the sled and moving through the woods to the city.

The next morning the tall man took the fir tree from the sled. His son and daughter helped him as they carried the happy tree to the front of the pleasant house in which they lived.

"Whatever can be happening to me?" thought the small fir tree. Neither the birds nor the wind had said anything about such an adventure, and he could not imagine what was going on.

A hole had been dug through the snow near the house. The man took the bag off the fir tree's roots. Then he stood him up straight, and filled the hole with rich black dirt. "How fine the little tree looks," the girl cried. And for once the fir didn't mind being called "little."

It was late on the day before Christmas, and the small tree once again was unhappy. True, he no longer needed to fear that he was going to be burned up a week or two after Christmas. But—

Now he would never be a Christmas tree!

Through the window in the house he could see another tree in the warm living room. It was this other tree that was being dressed up for Christmas while he stood lonely and forgotten in the cold snow. Here in the city the fir tree did not even have his friends from the woods to cheer him up. He was all alone.

Suddenly the front door flew open and light spilled forth on the frozen ground. Everyone, warmly dressed, came out of the house and walked up to the unhappy fir tree. In their hands they carried long strings of beautiful Christmas tree lights!

"Won't it be lovely!" the little girl said as she helped string the lights.

"Yes, indeed!" declared Mother. "All of our neighbors can see what a fine tree it is. And just think! We'll have the little fir tree to light up every year from now on."

After a minute the father called out, "All right, son, turn on the outdoor lights."

A hundred colored lights—green, orange, yellow, blue, white, and red—came to life in the unhappy little fir tree's snow-covered branches.

Only now the fir tree was no longer unhappy. He had not been forgotten. He sparkled with beautiful lights!

Best of all, people could enjoy him all year around. And he would be a Christmas tree, not just for a few weeks one year, but every Christmas for as long as he lived.

Ring Out, Wild Bells!

Ring out, wild bells, to the wild sky,
The flying cloud, the frosty light.
The year is dying in the night,
Ring out, wild bells, and let him die.

Ring out the old, ring in the new,
Ring, happy bells, across the snow;
The year is going, let him go;
Ring out the false, ring in the true.

Alfred, Lord Tennyson

Happy New Year in Many Lands

New Year's Day is a time for fun, feasting, and visiting. Did you ever wonder why?

In faraway China an old grandmother told her children a tale of why this is so. Here is her story.

Long, long ago people said that on the last day of the twelfth month, the earth would all be covered with water. Great rivers would run over the lands. No one would be saved.

When the people heard this news, they were very sad. They said to one another, "We are all going to die. Let us eat all the food we have. Let us dress in our prettiest clothes. We will be merry this night."

For days everyone was busy preparing for the feast. At last when everything was ready, the people of the village carried bowls of steaming food and plates of delicious little cakes to the house of their gods. After they prayed, each family sat together to eat their food and to talk. Then they went home. They shut their doors tightly and put heavy pieces of wood against them. They did not go to sleep but sat all night long watching and waiting.

For a Happy New Year in some parts of southern Europe, you must eat twelve grapes before the clock finishes striking twelve o'clock.

At last morning came. Carefully, at daybreak, they began to open their doors. There was no water! They were still alive! Quickly they ran from house to house to find their uncles, aunts, cousins, and friends. They drank tea and talked happily of their good luck.

From that day to this, people have been visiting and feasting and wishing each other good luck on New Year's Day. If you travel around the world you will see many different ways by which people in other lands express their good luck wishes.

Children in some countries of northern Europe go together from house to house. At each doorstep they "break in" the holiday by crashing a pot on the ground. The people in the home hear the noise. They open the door and ask the children to come in and have coffee and cakes with them.

While the bells ring out in some countries in the middle part of Europe, children try to touch a candy pig.

In Scotland, children call out from door to door. People open their doors to give the boys and girls apples and money.

The father awakens the family in some countries in Europe. At the breakfast table a child puts his finger into the "Good Book." Then the father reads to tell how the family will get along in the new year.

In parts of Norway and Scotland, the first person to ring your doorbell decides your luck. If it is a dark-haired man, it means good luck. A red-headed man or any woman brings bad luck all the year.

To all people in every land each New Year brings hope for better days, just as it did in China many hundreds of years ago.

The Twelve Months

There lived in a little house by the side of a road two sisters. One was kind and thoughtful. Mary was her name. Her sister, Rose, was unkind and selfish.

All day long Mary worked hard while Rose sat by the window and wished for things to happen.

One cold snowy day in January, Rose sat wishing it was springtime. After a while she called to her sister, "I wish I had some lovely purple flowers. Go this minute and gather some for me."

"But, sister, I can find no flowers in the snow," replied Mary.

Raising her voice, Rose cried crossly, "Go! And do not come back without the flowers!"

Mary went out into the woods. She had no warm coat. She hunted and hunted but could find no flowers. The ground was all covered with snow. At last, almost frozen, the girl saw a light in the distance. She struggled to get to the top of the hill. It, too, was covered with snow.

As Mary came over the top of the hill, she saw a strange sight. There was a huge fire. Around it sat twelve men in long coats. Three of the men wore coats as white as snow. Three had coats as green as the leaves of spring. Three were as yellow as gold. And three were as purple as grapes. All sat quietly watching the dancing flames.

The men looked up when they saw Mary. "What do you want?" asked one of the men who wore a white coat. His voice was hard and cold as he called to Mary.

"Please, sir," said Mary in a small voice, "let me sit by the fire and get warm. All day I have been searching for purple flowers. Now I am so cold. I cannot go home without them."

"Flowers! Flowers in wintertime!" shouted the great snowy man. "What a foolish girl!"

Mary began to cry. Then the man said to Mary, "Do not be afraid. We are the Twelve Months. My name is January."

After a minute January turned to a man in green. He handed him a long stick. Then he said to the man, "March, this is work for you to do. Take the high seat."

March stepped up and sat on a chair high above the others. He held the stick in the flames. The fire burned brightly. Warm spring winds began to blow. All the snow melted. The grass became a lovely soft green. Beautiful purple flowers were everywhere.

"Pick all you can carry," said the Months kindly, as Mary looked at the flowers.

Mary filled her arms. She thanked the men and ran home happily. Rose took the flowers from her sister without even a "Thank you." "Where did you get them?" she asked crossly.

"High up in the mountains. The ground was covered with beautiful purple blossoms," replied Mary.

The next morning Rose sat by the window again. She was very cross. "I want red strawberries for breakfast," she said in an angry voice. "Go at once and bring me some."

Mary started out sadly. She knew she could not find strawberries growing in the snow. On and on she walked. At last she came to the fire with the Twelve Months sitting around it. January had the high seat. Hungry and cold, the little girl said softly, "Please, sir, let me sit by the fire and get warm."

"What!" shouted January in a loud voice. "Are you here again? What do you want now?"

Mary hung her head. She was ashamed to tell the men what she wanted. Picking strawberries in January sounded so foolish. At last she told the Months that her sister would not let her come home until she found strawberries for breakfast.

Then January called to a Month who wore a yellow coat. "This is your work, June," and he handed him the stick. "Take the high seat and see what you can do."

In a few minutes the soft summer winds began to blow. The snow melted, and delicious red-ripe strawberries were everywhere.

"Fill your basket," said the Months kindly.

With her basket overflowing, Mary thanked the Months and ran home.

Rose was very surprised when she saw her sister come in with the basket full of red-ripe strawberries. "Where did you get them?" she asked in an angry voice. Quickly she took hold of the basket. Without stopping she ate every one of the berries. And she never even said "Thank you" or "Will you have some?"

Again, the next morning, Rose sat by the window wishing. "Today I will have purple grapes. Go right now and bring me some." Taking hold of her sister's shoulders, she pushed her out the door.

Once more Mary searched and searched. She walked until she was so tired and cold and hungry she thought she could walk no farther. At last she came to the fire of the Months.

"What brings you back this day?" asked January.

Weeping softly, Mary answered, "My sister will have purple grapes. And I cannot go home until I find them."

January handed the stick to a Month dressed in purple. "Here, September, you take the high seat. See what you can do."

September stepped up and sat in the great chair close to the fire. He held the stick in the hot flames for a minute. Wonderful things happened. A cold wind began to blow. Trees were covered with beautiful red and gold-colored leaves. The snow disappeared. Large purple grapes hung in bunches everywhere.

"Take twelve grapes only," said September.

Mary put twelve grapes in her basket. Then she thanked the Months once again, and hurried home.

When Rose saw that there were but twelve grapes, she was very angry, indeed. Stamping her foot, she said in a sharp voice, "I will get all the grapes." With that, she put on her coat and rushed out the door.

After walking for a long time, Rose came to the fire of the Months.

"Who are you? What do you want?" asked January in a cold voice.

"That is nothing to you," replied Rose in a very unpleasant voice.

Then a strange thing happened. January sat in the high seat. He held his stick over the flames. Immediately the fire went out. Cold, biting winds began to blow. Heavy snow covered the earth. The Twelve Months disappeared. Rose could not move. She was all alone. She cried out for help but no one heard her.

Mary waited and waited but Rose never came home. However, Mary was not lonely. The Twelve Months took turns visiting her. Each one brought lovely gifts.

The Four Winds

High and low
The spring winds blow!
They take the kites that the boys have made,
And carry them off high into the air;
They roll the little girls' hats away,
And merrily whip their flowing hair.

High and low
The summer winds blow!
They dance and play with the garden flowers,
And bend the grasses and yellow grain;
They rock the bird in her hanging nest,
And splash the rain on the window-pane.

High and low
The autumn winds blow!
They frighten the birds and blossoms away,
And chase the dry leaves over the ground;
They shake the branches of all the trees,
And blow ripe nuts and apples around.

High and low
The winter winds blow!
They fill the holes with piles of snow,
And sweep on the hills a pathway clear;
They hurry the children along to school,
And whistle a song for the
Happy New Year!

Author unknown

My Kingdom for an April Fool

Do you remember the story of Proserpina who was carried off by Pluto to the lower world? Look back at the story of "Why Winter Comes." Here you will find the beginning of April Fool.

'Tis said that Ceres went all over the earth hunting her daughter. She kept hearing the cries of Proserpina and searched everywhere. But always she found only a voice—so her search became only a "fool's hunt."

Proserpina returned to the earth at the end of March. Great was the joy of the Romans—so great that they made a feast which lasted for a whole week. At the end of the merrymaking, people played tricks on each other.

Today the last day of the feast of the return of Prosperina is kept on April 1. People play tricks. Everyone wants to be an April Fool, just like the king in this tale of old.

Many years ago there lived a king in a beautiful land. He was not happy. Indeed he was sad. Every first of April all the people in the kingdom went about playing tricks on each other. But never had anyone tricked the king.

The king was quite unhappy. He sent out an order saying that he wanted to be an April Fool. In fact, he declared he would give half his kingdom to anyone who could fool him. Now, you see, he thought he was so wise that no one could play a trick on him.

By the time the next April first came around everyone had forgotten except the king's page.

"Oh, breadsticks!" said the cook, when the page reminded him. "Imagine fooling the king! He is too wise for that."

"Oh, bluebells!" said the old gardener. "Imagine fooling the king! He is too wise for that."

"Oh, dusters!" said the housekeeper. "Imagine fooling the king. He is too wise for that."

No one would even try. Then the page thought and thought. "I have it!" Up he jumped and away he ran.

The evening of April first was bright. The stars seemed to be dancing in the sky. After supper the king went out walking. Upon coming to a small lake he heard a small voice cry out, "Help me! Help me! I have fallen into the lake."

The king hurried to the edge of the lake. Again the voice cried out, "Help me! I am a star-fairy. I fell out of the sky into the lake. And I cannot swim."

The good king looked into the water. In front of him, as plain as could be, he could see the little star in the lake. Bending over, he tried to reach it. But try as he may he could not seem to get hold of the little star.

Again the voice cried out for help.

"Hold on!" called the king, "I will save you yet." With one last try, the king reached way over. Splash! Into the water he fell.

Dripping with water the king climbed out of the lake. Just then a voice called loudly, "April Fool! April Fool!" And with that the king's page came running from behind some trees.

"Half the kingdom!" called the boy. "You promised half of your kingdom to anyone who could fool you."

"Half the kingdom! Bread-sticks!" answered the king. And he looked cross. Now that he was an April Fool he did not seem to like it very much.

The king looked up at the stars in the sky. Then he looked down and saw them all dancing in the lake. He began to laugh. "Half a kingdom for you, my boy! Half a kingdom you will have!"

When the people of the kingdom heard the news, all they could say was, "*Breadsticks and bluebells! Imagine that!*"

Holiday Games

Each holiday brings special games that are fun to play. Boys and girls of long ago enjoyed games, also. Perhaps your mother and father had some favorite games they played when they were children. Here are two they might remember. Play them and see if you think they are fun, too.

April Fool!

Everyone comes ready to do a magic trick. After all the tricks have been played, the group decides which one was the best.

The first player may hold up a piece of black art paper. He asks the children to tell what they see on the picture. When they say there is no picture, he tells his story. He might say, "This picture shows a black cat sleeping in a dark room at night."

The Gardener

The leader is called the "gardener." He gives each player the name of some flower. Then he tells a story about his garden.

Each time the gardener tells about a flower, the player who has that name stands, turns, and sits down again.

When he tells about gathering many flowers, everyone changes seats. At this time the gardener tries to get a seat. The player without a chair becomes the gardener. Or if anyone fails to stand when his flower is called, he becomes the gardener. He then tells about his flowers.

Just for Today

Father, for tomorrow and its needs
I do not pray:
Keep me from doing things that are wrong
Just for today.
Let me be honest in all my work
And fair in play,
Help me to be slow to do *my* will
But quick to obey,
Teach me to be kind in word and deed
Just for today.

Answers to Riddles

Page 34:

- • Two. Inside and outside.
- •• He had to pack his trunk.
- ••• The letter *a*.
- •••• Three (x - x - x).
- ••••• They were facing each other.

The fairy trick with 9—When you add 0 after a number you really multiply by 10. So the number 9 is 1 less than 10. So you see when you multiply by 10 and subtract the number, you really are multiplying by 9.

Page 124:

- • A star.
- •• A bed.
- ••• Tomorrow.
- •••• A river.

Page 172:

The farm—To cut the land into 4 parts of equal size and shape (1) draw 2 lines to make 3 squares; (2) draw lines to cut each big square into 4 little squares; (3) give each group of people 3 small squares of land.

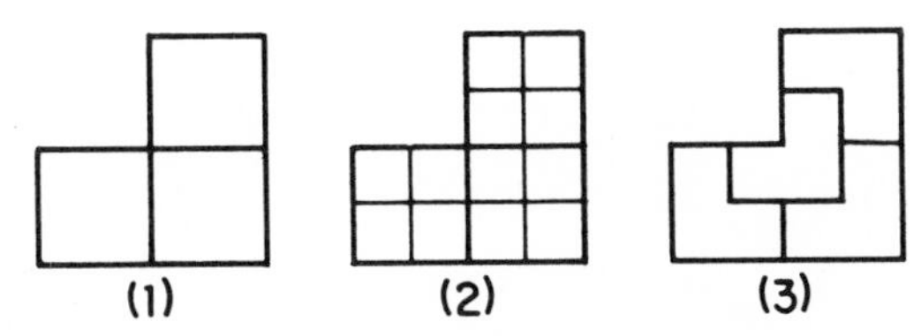

Page 186:

A baby crawls on four feet (two hands and two feet). This is the morning of life (early life). In middle life (noon), a man walks on two feet. In later life (evening) a man walks with the help of a stick. He needs a cane in old age (three legs).

Names of Storybook Friends

Friends are important. You have made many storybook friends in *Magic and Laughter*. You will meet some of them again and again in your reading. Will you know who they are and how to say their names rightly? Try these riddles to see.

To play the game, first read the riddle. Think who the friend is. Next, find the name in the list of "Sound Spellings" on page 239. See if you can say the word exactly right. Watch the letter markings. Now find the name in the list of "Names of Some Storybook Friends" and say it again.

Some of the names in the list you did not use to answer the riddles. Can you make up riddles for these names? Try it and see whether other children can guess your riddles.

On page 240 you will find more names of people.

Riddles

She was the daughter of the goddess of all growing things. One day the king of the underworld carried her off. Every year she had to spend six months underground because she ate six seeds. Her return to earth marks the coming of spring.

. . . . .

As a young boy he traveled from Venice to China with his father and uncle. They were the first merchants to make the dangerous trip from Europe to China. They lived in China many years.

. . . . .

He traveled to the Hawaiian Islands to help the people who lived in the leper colony. Although he had no money, he had great courage. Through his hard work, the lepers built better homes. They built schools and churches. Doctors came to help the sick. He gave to the lepers the greatest gift of all—himself.

. . . . .

He was a very poor man who worked hard. His brother was mean and selfish. One day he learned a magic word which made him very rich.

. . . . .

He was a mean and unkind god of the Northland. One day he stole the golden hair from the wife of a god. Then he had to go to the underground world of the dwarfs to get new golden hair for her.

Sound Spellings of Storybook Names

ä′ lē bä′ bä	prō sur′ pə nə
sē′ rēz	mär′ kō pō′ lō
hī′ dē	pay′ drō
plōō′ tō	lō′ kē
thôr	dā′ mĭ ən
zûrk′ sēz	lĭ ŏn′ ə dəs

Names of Some Storybook Friends

Heidi	Ali Baba
Pluto	Loki
Marco Polo	Damien
Ceres	Xerxes
Leonidas	Proserpina
Pedro	Thor

Key for Letter Markings

If you have trouble working out the sound spellings of the words, look at the key below.

Say: ā as in *make* — ō as in *bone*
ä as in *arm* — ŏ as in *hot*
ē as in *be* — ô as in *or*
ī as in *like* — ōō as in *cool*
ĭ as in *it* — û as in *fur*
ə is any vowel that is not pronounced clearly

Word List

One of the unique features of *Magic and Laughter* is the close correlation of the vocabulary with the vocabularies of leading basal reading series. If *Magic and Laughter* is used after the completion of the Fourth Reader of your basal reading series, pupils will encounter only a very few new words in *Magic and Laughter.*

A list of words new to the basic-reader vocabulary which you use in your classroom, together with the page numbers on which these words first appear in *Magic and Laughter,* is found in the Teachers' Manual for *Magic and Laughter.*

Names of people and places found often in literature, as well as in *Magic and Laughter,* are listed here as an aid to the teacher in helping children learn those which are new to them.

Literary Names: People

Ali Baba
Archimedes
Arthur
Cassim
Ceres
Columbus
Dick Whittington
Eric
Father Damien
Fritz
Grace Darling
Heidi
Jupiter
Kay
Kirsten
Leonidas
Loki
Mafatu
Marco Polo
Merlin
Neteland
Otto
Pedro
Peter
Pierre
Pluto
Proserpina
Robinson
Roland
Rudi
Thor
Truck
Vulcan
Xerxes

Literary Names: Places

China
Europe
France
Germany
Greece
Hawaii
Ireland
London
Mexico
Molokai
Norway
Pacific
Paricutin
Rome
Scotland
Sparta
Switzerland
Thermopylae
Venice